The Low GI Cookbook

OTHER LOW GI
& NEW GLUCOSE REVOLUTION TITLES

Cookbooks

The Low GI Diet Cookbook: 100 Simple, Delicious Smart-Carb Recipes

The New Glucose Revolution Low GI Vegetarian Cookbook

The New Glucose Revolution Low GI Family Cookbook

Shopping and Eating Out

The New Glucose Revolution Shopper's Guide to GI Values 2010

Diabetes and Prediabetes

The New Glucose Revolution for Diabetes

The New Glucose Revolution Low GI Guide to Diabetes

What Makes My Blood Glucose Go Up . . . And Down?:
101 Frequently Asked Questions about Your Blood Glucose Level

Weight Loss

The Low GI Diet Revolution: The Definitive Science-Based Weight Loss Plan

The New Glucose Revolution Low GI Guide to Losing Weight

Heart Health

The New Glucose Revolution Low GI Guide to Your Heart
and the Metabolic Syndrome

PCOS

The Low GI Guide to Living Well with PCOS

Celiac Disease or Gluten Intolerance

The New Glucose Revolution Low GI Guide to Gluten-free Living

The Low GI Cookbook

90 Simple, Delicious Good-Carb Recipes to Complement the Nutrisystem® Program

Dr. Jennie Brand-Miller • Kaye Foster-Powell
Joanna McMillan

Da Capo

LIFE
LONG

A Member of the Perseus Books Group

The Low GI Cookbook: 90 Simple, Delicious, Good-Carb Recipes to Complement the Nutrisystem® Program

Photography copyright © 2005 Hachette Livre Australia Pty Limited
Photography copyright © 2005 p. 16 Shaun Cato-Symonds; p. 31 John Lee; p. 115 Andre Martin

Text copyright © 2005, 2011 by Jennie Brand-Miller, Kaye Foster-Powell, and Joanna McMillan-Price
Recipes copyright © 2005 pp. 116, 128 Johanna Burani; p. 102 Chris and Carolyn Caldicott; pp. 33, 124 Judy Davie; p. 31 Margaret Fulton; pp. 28, 79 (Tagine spice mix), 134 Liz and Ian Hemphill; pp. 16, 52 Julie Le Clerc; p. 27 Dr Nancy Longnecker; pp. 81, 103 Isobel McMillan; pp. 40, 68, 83 Jill McMillan; pp. 63, 64, 87 Luke Mangan; pp. 73, 85 Lynne Mullins; p. 130 Emma Pemberton; pp. 75, 97, 112 Professor Steffan Rössner; pp. 115, 122 Catherine Saxelby; pp. 88, 91, 134 Carol Selva Rajah; p. 13 (Toasted muesli) Dr Rosemary Stanton; p. 94 Michelle Trute.

This edition was published in somewhat different form in Australia by Hachette Livre Australia. This edition is published by arrangement with Hachette Livre Australia.

Designer: Michelle Cutler
Editor: Kim Rowney
Photographer: Ian Hoftstetter
Stylist (recipes): Stephanie Souvlis
Home economist: Lee Currie
Color separation by Colourscan, Singapore

Cataloging-in-Publication data for this book is available from the Library of Congress.

First Da Capo Press edition 2011
ISBN: 978-0-7382-1519-8

Published by Da Capo Press
A Member of the Perseus Books Group
www.dacapopress.com

Note: The information in this book is true and complete to the best of our knowledge. This book is intended only as an informative guide for those wishing to know more about health issues. In no way is this book intended to replace, countermand, or conflict with the advice given to you by your own physician. The ultimate decision concerning care should be made between you and your doctor. We strongly recommend you follow his or her advice. Information in this book is general and is offered with no guarantees on the part of the authors or Da Capo Press. The authors and publisher disclaim all liability in connection with the use of this book. The names and identifying details of people associated with events described in this book have been changed. Any similarity to actual persons is coincidental.

Da Capo Press books are available at special discounts for bulk purchases in the U.S. by corporations, institutions, and other organizations. For more information, please contact the Special Markets Department at the Perseus Books Group, 2300 Chestnut Street, Suite 200, Philadelphia, PA, 19103, or call (800) 810-4145, ext. 5000, or e-mail special.markets@perseusbooks.com.

10 9 8 7 6 5 4 3 2 1

CONTENTS

FOREWORD

by Bruce Daggy, PhD, Vice President of Research and Development, Nutrisystem, Inc.

Nutrisystem is delighted to have partnered with the authors of *The Low GI Cookbook* to create this useful guide for low Glycemic Index (GI) eating. The term "low Glycemic Index" dates back to 1981, and this approach to healthy eating has now been the subject of hundreds of studies. Even before 1981, research had raised concerns about the long-term health effects of the typical "Western" diet, high in refined sugar and low in dietary fiber. In 1800, refined sugar was essentially absent from our food supply; it is now present in abundance. Just one 12 oz. can of a very popular high fructose corn syrup sweetened soft drink delivers 39 g of sugar—when the recommended intake of added sugar is less than 25 g per day! Healthcare experts are increasingly convinced that our "bad carbs" diet is contributing to the rise of diseases such as diabetes, and to obesity itself. This is not to say that all sugar is bad; many fruits provide sugars, and even the sugars we add to our foods and beverages are not a big concern in moderation. In recent years, however, moderation has become difficult. We are consuming more foods that are high in sugar and/or fat, with the result that a small serving size can pack in a large number of calories. Before we know it, we've overeaten. Studies suggest that the average adult is consuming hundreds more calories per day now than would have been the case 30 years ago. We need to go back to a diet that is more filling with fewer calories. We need to return to the "good carbs" diet of yesteryear.

By 2003, Nutrisystem was convinced by the evidence of the beneficial effects of a low GI diet, and made this feature a core principle of our portion-controlled meal plans. Our nutrition team worked to develop entrées that, when combined with grocery additions including fruits, vegetables, and low fat dairy, would result in meal plans consistent with clinical studies showing a health benefit. We aimed to remove most of the guesswork from following this approach; we even delivered the food to our customers' homes, color-coded by meal occasion. With our entrées, there was nothing to weigh, measure, or count. That simplicity produced results, but left us with a question: how do we help our members stick with this approach once they are no longer buying all of their entrées from us? The average consumer is not going to clinically test a recipe to know that is fits into a low GI program!

Which leads us to this book. For those occasions when you want to cook something both tasty and good for you (and your family), and consistent with a Nutrisystem® weight loss or weight maintenance plan, this book shows you how. Bon appétit!

INTRODUCTION

The *Low GI Cookbook* is a wonderful accompaniment to the Nutrisystem® program. This cookbook offers a variety of delicious breakfast, lunch, dinner, and even dessert recipes which reinforce the value of eating perfectly portioned®, low-fat, low glycemic, good carb meals, on which the success of the Nutrisystem programs are based. These meals and snacks can complement your Nutrisystem® weight loss program or help you maintain your weight loss by teaching you the types of foods and portion sizes to enjoy.

Each recipe has been reviewed by the Nutrisystem registered dietitians and meets the nutritional standards of the Nutrisystem® Men's and Women's Basic Programs. Sodium and sugar content of each recipe is provided for those individuals following a more restricted diet. Whether you are trying to lose weight or maintain your weight loss, the recipes in this book offer a nutritional profile with the proper amount of calories, fat, saturated fat, sugar, cholesterol, and sodium, while providing heart-healthy fiber and lean protein to help keep you full and satisfied.

Refer to the Nutrisystem meal equivalents listed under the nutritional profile of each recipe to determine how one recipe serving fits into your Nutrisystem® weight loss or weight maintenance meal plan. As you transition to preparing low-GI meals, remember the core principles of the Nutrisystem program to ensure your continued success:

- Enjoy small, frequent meals throughout the day
- Consume foods high in fiber, and low in fat, sugar, and sodium
- Use your Nutrisystem meal planner to help you maintain proper portion sizes at meals and snacks and track your intake
- Record your weight loss
- Engage in physical activity most days of the week
- Get support through the Nutrisystem online community or 24/7 counseling service

WHY THE LOW GI DIET WORKS

Low GI foods have the unique ability to keep you feeling fuller for longer and to maximize your engine revs (metabolic rate) during active weight loss. And, as we all know, the higher your metabolic rate, the easier your weight loss. By slowing down digestion and absorption of carbohydrates, the low GI diet steadies both your blood glucose and insulin levels, stopping the roller-coaster ride that spells hunger and bingeing. And by bringing down insulin, your body will burn more body fat.

THE SEVEN GUIDELINES OF THE LOW GI DIET

We believe that choosing low GI foods is one of the most important dietary choices you can make for your long-term health, energy and weight control. As well as identifying your best low GI choices, our guidelines give you a blueprint for healthy eating for life.

1 EAT SEVEN OR MORE SERVINGS OF FRUIT AND VEGETABLES EVERY DAY

Being high in fiber, and therefore filling, and low in fat (apart from olives and avocado, which contain "good" fats), fruit and vegetables play a central role in the low GI diet. They are also bursting with vitamins, minerals, antioxidants and phytochemicals, which will give you the glow of good health. Aim to eat at least two servings of fruit and five servings of vegetables daily, preferably of three or more different colors. A serving is about one medium-sized piece of fruit, or half a cup of cooked vegetables or one cup of raw.

Most vegetables have very little carbohydrate so do not have a GI. Potato, however, has a high GI, so if you are a big potato eater, try to replace some with low GI alternatives such as sweet corn, sweet potato, taro and yam. As for green and salad vegetables, you can eat them freely, so pile your plate high and remember that variety is the key.

Most fruit have a low GI, the lowest being apples and citrus (such as oranges and grapefruit) and stone fruit (such as peaches and nectarines). However, there's no need to limit high GI fruit such as watermelon or cantaloupe because even a large serving of these healthy fruit contains very little carbohydrate.

2 EAT LOW GI BREADS AND CEREALS

The type of bread and cereals you eat affects the GI of your diet the most. Mixed grain breads, sourdough, traditional rolled oats, bulgur wheat, pearl barley, pasta, noodles and certain types of rice are just a few examples of low GI cereal foods. One of the easiest and most important changes you can make to lower the overall GI of your diet is to choose a low GI bread. Most people need at least four servings of grains a day (very active people need more), where a serving is one slice of bread or half a cup of pasta.

3 EAT MORE LEGUMES INCLUDING BEANS, CHICKPEAS AND LENTILS

Whether you buy dried beans, chickpeas or lentils and cook them yourself at home or opt for convenient, time-saving canned varieties, you are choosing one of nature's lowest GI foods. These nutritional "power packs" are high in fiber, low in calories and provide a valuable source of protein, carbohydrate, B vitamins, folate, iron, zinc and magnesium. Enjoy them at least twice a week for meals or snacks.

4 EAT NUTS MORE REGULARLY

Although nuts are high in fat (averaging around 50 percent), it is largely unsaturated fat, so they make a healthy substitute for snacks such as cookies, cakes, pastries, potato chips and chocolate. They also contain relatively little carbohydrate, so most do not have a GI. The exceptions are cashews and peanuts, which are low GI. Nuts contain a variety of antioxidants and are also one of the richest sources of vitamin E—in fact, a small handful of mixed nuts provides more than 20 percent of your recommended daily intake.

5 EAT MORE FISH AND SEAFOOD

Fish and seafood do not have a GI because they are a source of protein, not carbohydrate. Increased fish consumption is linked to a reduced risk of coronary heart disease, improvements in mood, lower rates of depression, better blood fat levels and enhanced immunity. The likely protective components are the omega-3 fatty acids. Our bodies only make small amounts of these fatty acids and so we rely on our diet, especially fish and seafood, to obtain them. One to three meals of fish each week is a good habit to get into to start reaping all the health benefits. The richest sources of omega-3 fats are oily fish such as Atlantic and smoked salmon, and swordfish. However, canned sardines, mackerel and salmon and, to a lesser extent, tuna are also good sources. Look for canned fish packed in water, olive oil, canola oil, tomato sauce or brine, and drain well.

Due to the risk of high levels of mercury in certain species of fish, the Food and Drug Administration (FDA) recently advised that although pregnant women, nursing mothers, women planning a pregnancy, and young children can consume a variety of fish as part of a healthy diet, they should avoid the consumption of certain species. Shark, swordfish, king mackerel, and tilefish should not be consumed, because these long-lived larger fish contain the highest levels of mercury. Pregnant women should select a variety of other fish—shellfish, canned fish such as light tuna, smaller ocean fish, or farm-raised fish. The FDA says you can safely eat up to 12 oz of cooked fish per week, with a typical serving size being 3 to 6 oz.

6 EAT LEAN RED MEATS, POULTRY AND EGGS

These protein foods do not have a GI because they are not sources of carbohydrate. Red meat, however, is the best source of iron you can get. Good iron status can increase your energy levels and improve your exercise tolerance. We suggest eating moderate amounts (approximately 3 ounces) of lean red meat occasionally and accompanying it with a salad or vegetables. Eggs and skinless chicken also provide options for variety.

7 EAT LOW-FAT DAIRY PRODUCTS

Milk, cheese, ice cream, yogurt, buttermilk and custard are the richest sources of calcium in our diet. By replacing full fat dairy foods with reduced fat, low-fat or fat-free versions, you will reduce your saturated fat intake and actually boost your calcium intake.

ACTIVITY—THE OTHER SIDE OF THE ENERGY EQUATION

The low GI diet deals not only with what goes in your mouth (energy intake), but with physical activity (energy output). This is the critical side of the energy equation. If you don't build physical activity into your life, you have very little chance of changing your body shape for life.

Exercising while you lose weight will help you maximize fat loss and minimize lean muscle loss. This means you get leaner faster. Throughout *The Low GI Cookbook*, we have included activity tips to help you stay on track because we know that the people most likely to keep the weight off are those who raise their activity levels and make exercise a natural part of life.

WHAT IS THE GI?

The GI (glycemic index), a proven measure of how fast carbohydrates hit the bloodstream, helps you choose the right amount and type of carbohydrates for your health and well-being. Foods with a high GI value contain carbohydrates that will cause a dramatic rise in your blood glucose levels, while foods with a low GI value contain carbohydrates that will have a lesser impact.

LOW GI < 55
MEDIUM (OR MODERATE) GI 56–69
HIGH GI > 70

HOW OUR LOW GI RECIPES GIVE YOU A HEALTHY BALANCE

We have chosen recipes that will give you a healthy balance of all the nutrients your body needs. We have analyzed the recipes, and the nutrient profile* includes the GI (glycemic index), energy, fat, protein, carbohydrate, fiber, sugar and sodium content per serving. Here we explain the role each nutrient plays in the low GI diet.

GI An emphasis on low GI carbs such as pasta, legumes, sweet potato, whole grains, fruit and dairy products ensures most of our recipes have a low GI. The value we give is our best estimate of the range in which the GI of each recipe falls.

ENERGY DENSITY The calorie count per serving of each recipe indicates its energy density. This is important for weight control because it's easy to overconsume calories when your diet is based on energy-dense foods. By incorporating lots of vegetables, salads, fruit and high fiber foods into recipes, they retain a lower energy density. Limit portion sizes of higher calorie foods to help manage weight.

FATS Forget what you've been told about low fat and learn the new fat message—it's not all bad. The type of fat is more important for your health than the total amount. Most of us need to eat more of certain types of fat for optimal health. These fats include the omega-3 fats found in fish and seafood, and omega-neutral monounsaturated fats found in olive and canola oils. You'll find we have incorporated the "good" fats in our recipes by using nuts, oily fish, avocado, olives and olive oil.

PROTEIN Sufficient protein in the diet is important for weight control because, compared to carbohydrate and fat, protein makes us feel more satisfied immediately after eating and reduces hunger between meals. Protein also increases our metabolic rate for 1–3 hours after eating. This means we burn more energy by the minute compared with the increase that occurs after eating carbohydrates or fats. Even though this is a relatively small difference, it may be important in long-term weight control. Our recipes include the highest quality, lowest fat protein sources of lean meat, fish, shellfish, tofu and legumes.

CARBOHYDRATE Most of our recipes have a carbohydrate base but the emphasis is always on low GI because the slow digestion and absorption of these foods will fill you up, trickle fuel into your engine at a more useable rate, and keep you satisfied for longer. The actual amount of carbohydrate consumed at each meal may be relevant to those with diabetes and those who monitor their blood glucose levels.

We've used moderate amounts of refined sugar (medium GI) in our recipes for healthy desserts and sweet treats. The World Health Organization says "a moderate intake of sugar-rich foods can provide for a palatable and nutritious diet." So, enjoy refined sugar, using it judiciously to make nutritious foods more palatable. Just be mindful of sugar in liquid form (such as soft drinks and fruit juices) because they are easy to overconsume.

FIBER Experts recommend a daily fiber intake of 25–35 grams, but most people fall short of that recommendation. The low GI diet will get you a lot closer to the target because most of our recipes are brimming with fiber. This means they will not only keep you regular but will also help lower your blood glucose, your cholesterol levels and reduce your risk of many chronic diseases.

SODIUM Sodium is the part of salt that can increase blood pressure. We want you to minimize consumption of salt and salty foods, so you will find, in most cases, salt hasn't been included as an ingredient in our recipes. Because many people follow low sodium diets, we have included the sodium content for each recipe.

* Some recipes were revised to reduce sodium and/or calorie content. All recipes were analyzed using Genesis® R&D nutrient software from ESHA Research.

HOW TO USE THIS BOOK

Two reasons the low GI diet is so easy to live with long-term are that there are no special foods to buy and you can enjoy three balanced meals a day, including a dessert or indulgence at dinner and snacks in between, if you wish. So, to keep making it easy for you, that's how we have organized the chapters in our cookbook—Breakfast, Lunches and Light Meals, Soups and Salads, Dinner, and Desserts and Sweet Treats. We have also included a section called Basic Recipes, where you will find the spice blends we use in a number of recipes, along with some popular side dishes and accompaniments such as tabbouli and saffron pilaf.

To keep making low GI eating easy every day and every meal, turn to the section called Your Low GI Foods. Here's where we explain what to stock in your pantry, refrigerator and freezer.

The recipes are generally quick (see the preparation and cooking times) and easy to make, and full of healthy ingredients. If a recipe is rich in particular micronutrients, we have identified them for you in the recipe introduction. We have also included cook's tips, with information on recipe shortcuts, preparation hints and shopping tips. And, of course, there are the activity ideas to help you stay motivated and make exercise and physical activity a natural part of your life.

We hope that you enjoy preparing and eating these meals as much as we do.

NOTE
The recipes in this book use common household measurements. All cups and spoon measures are level. Our recipes use large eggs with an average weight of 2 oz. All herbs used in the recipes are fresh unless otherwise stated.

BREAKFAST

MAKE BREAKFAST A PRIORITY—IT'S THE MOST
IMPORTANT MEAL OF YOUR DAY, RECHARGING
YOUR BRAIN AND SPEEDING UP YOUR
METABOLISM AFTER AN OVERNIGHT "FAST."
THESE DELICIOUS BREAKFASTS AND BRUNCHES,
FILLED WITH FRESH INGREDIENTS AND
PREPARED WITH MINIMUM FUSS, WILL
NOURISH YOUR BODY AND SUSTAIN YOU
THROUGH THE MORNING.

PORTOBELLO MUSHROOMS WITH RICOTTA AND ROASTED TOMATOES SERVES 4

There's nothing quite like tomatoes that have ripened in the sunshine on the vine. The next best thing is to buy tomatoes still on the vine—you will find they have developed a fuller flavor. Preparation time: 10 minutes Cooking time: 15 minutes

16 cherry tomatoes on the vine
1 tablespoon balsamic vinegar
2 tablespoons extra-virgin olive oil
freshly ground black pepper
juice of 1 lemon
1 tablespoon chopped dill
4 medium portobello mushrooms, stems trimmed
½ cup low-fat ricotta cheese
4 thick slices sourdough or grainy bread, to serve

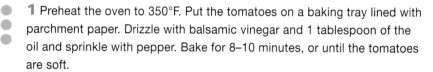

1 Preheat the oven to 350°F. Put the tomatoes on a baking tray lined with parchment paper. Drizzle with balsamic vinegar and 1 tablespoon of the oil and sprinkle with pepper. Bake for 8–10 minutes, or until the tomatoes are soft.

2 Combine the remaining oil, lemon juice and dill in a bowl and season with a little pepper. Brush the mushrooms generously with the oil marinade, then place, stem-side down, on a heated grill or in a frying pan and cook for 3 minutes. Turn the mushrooms over, crumble the ricotta over the top and spoon over the remaining marinade. Cook for 2–3 minutes, or until the mushrooms are soft.

3 Serve the mushrooms and roasted tomatoes with toasted sourdough or grainy bread.

ACTIVITY TIPS

If possible, walk to work, or at least part of the way, or walk the children to school.

Keep comfortable shoes at work so that you never have an excuse not to exercise.

GI LOW

Per serving (1 mushroom, 4 tomatoes, ¼ Tbsp of oil, ⅛ cup of cheese)
200 Cal, 10 g fat (saturated 2 g),
10 g protein, 21 g carbohydrate, 4 g fiber, 7 g sugar,
190 mg sodium

Equals: 1 Nutrisystem® Breakfast + 1 Dairy

FRUITY QUINOA PORRIDGE SERVES 4

Quinoa (pronounced keen-wa) is a tiny, quick-cooking grain. It is rich in nutrients, has less than 5 percent fat, with no saturated fat, and a low GI of 53. Quinoa has a mild, nutty flavor and a slightly chewy texture. Look for it in larger supermarkets or health food stores. Preparation time: 10 minutes Cooking time: 15 minutes

1 cup quinoa
2 cups skim milk
1 apple, chopped with skin on
1/3 cup raisins
1 cinnamon stick or 1/2 teaspoon ground cinnamon
1 tablespoon pure floral honey
1/2 cup warm skim milk, extra, to serve

1 Put the quinoa in a sieve and rinse well under cold running water. Tip the quinoa into a saucepan, then pour in the milk. Bring to a boil, then reduce the heat and simmer for 5 minutes. Add the apple, raisins and cinnamon and simmer for 5–6 minutes, or until all of the liquid is absorbed. Remove the cinnamon stick, if using.

2 Serve the quinoa porridge in small bowls. Drizzle the honey over the top and serve with the extra skim milk.

GI LOW Ⓖ

Per serving (1 cup + 1/4 cup warm milk)
310 Cal, 2.5 g fat (saturated 0 g),
13 g protein, 60 g carbohydrate, 5 g fiber, 19 g sugar,
90 mg sodium

Equals: 1 Nutrisystem® Breakfast + 1 Dairy + 1 Fruit

BREAKFAST FRUIT LOAF MAKES 12 SLICES

Although it is difficult to predict the GI of baked foods containing flour, we know that fruit loaves have a lower GI because some of the flour is replaced with dried fruit. This loaf is also packed with the fiber needed for a healthy digestive system.

Soaking time: 30 minutes Preparation time: 10 minutes Cooking time: 1–1¼ hours

3/4 cup All-Bran® cereal
1 1/3 cups skim milk
1 1/2 cups whole wheat
self-rising flour
1 teaspoon baking powder
3/4 cup raisins
2/3 cup dried apricots, chopped
into small pieces
1/4 cup pitted prunes, chopped
into small pieces
1/3 cup dark muscovado sugar
4 tablespoons pure floral honey

1 Put the bran cereal in a bowl, pour over the milk and soak for 30 minutes. Preheat the oven to 350°F.

2 Sift the flour and baking powder into a bowl and stir in the bran cereal mixture, along with any bran left in the sieve. Stir in the dried fruit, sugar and honey and mix well.

3 Spoon the mixture into a non-stick 2 lb loaf pan (or brush the pan with oil to prevent sticking) and level off the top. Bake for 1–1¼ hours, or until the loaf is baked through and golden brown on top.

4 Allow the loaf to cool a little in the pan before turning it out onto a wire rack to cool completely. The loaf will store for several weeks if wrapped in foil and kept in an airtight container.

COOK'S TIP
Muscovado sugar, sometimes called Barbados sugar, is a very dark brown unrefined sugar. Light and dark muscovado sugars both contain molasses; the darker variety is stickier and has a stronger molasses flavor than the light. If you can't find muscovado, use a good-quality dark brown sugar.

G GI LOW
Per slice (1/12 loaf)
150 Cal, .5 g fat (saturated 0 g),
4 g protein, 36 g carbohydrate, 4 g fiber, 12 g sugar,
30 mg sodium

Equals: 1 Nutrisystem® Breakfast

FRENCH TOAST WITH BERRY COMPOTE SERVES 4

Enjoy this berry compote using your favorite mix of fresh or frozen berries—strawberries, raspberries, blackberries, blueberries or boysenberries. Berries don't ripen once they're picked, so choose carefully—the deeply colored ones tend to be the sweetest and have the most flavor. Preparation time: 5 minutes Cooking time: 15 minutes

2 cups mixed berries
2 eggs
2 tablespoons low-fat milk
4 slices whole wheat raisin bread or fruit loaf
2 tablespoons sugar free maple syrup

1 Put the berries in a small saucepan and gently heat until the berries are warm and have softened.

2 Meanwhile, break the eggs into a flat-bottomed dish, add the milk and whisk with a fork to combine. Add the slices of fruit bread and coat well, on both sides, with the egg mixture.

3 Heat a non-stick frying pan over medium heat and dry-fry 2 slices of the eggy bread for about 3 minutes on each side, or until brown. Repeat with the remaining 2 slices. Cut the bread in half and serve topped with the warm berries and 2 teaspoons of the maple syrup drizzled over the top of each.

COOK'S TIP
Berries are best eaten as soon as possible after you have purchased them. If you need to keep them for a day or two, here's how to minimize mold. Take them out of the container and place on a couple of layers of paper towel, cover loosely with plastic wrap and store in the refrigerator. Don't wash them until you're ready to use them.

GI LOW G

Per serving (1 slice of bread, 1/2 cup of berry mixture,
1/2 Tbsp maple syrup)
170 Cal, 3.5 g fat (saturated 1 g),
6 g protein, 29 g carbohydrate, 3 g fiber, 11 g sugar,
160 mg sodium

Equals: 1 Nutrisystem® Breakfast

STRAWBERRY YOGURT CRUNCH SERVES 4

Although nuts and seeds are high in fat, research shows that people who eat them often tend to be slimmer and healthier. This is because the fat in nuts and seeds is mainly unsaturated (the healthy kind of fat), we probably don't absorb all of it, and they are packed with other essential nutrients and fiber. Preparation time: 10 minutes Cooking time: 1–2 minutes

1/3 cup mixed raw nuts, such as cashews, peanuts, pistachios and almonds
2 tablespoons sunflower seeds
2 tablespoons pumpkin seeds
3 cups low-fat natural yogurt
1 large mango, sliced
1 1/4 cups strawberries, sliced
4 teaspoons pure floral honey

1 Heat a non-stick frying pan over medium heat and add the raw nuts and seeds. Dry-fry them for 1–2 minutes, stirring continuously until browned (take care as the nuts will burn very quickly). Remove from the heat and, when cool enough to handle, roughly chop with a large knife.

2 Take four glasses and spoon a little yogurt into the bottom of each one. Divide the mango slices between the glasses, top with another layer of yogurt, then finish with a layer of sliced strawberries.

3 Drizzle the honey over the strawberries and sprinkle the toasted nut and seed mixture over the top.

Ⓖ GI LOW
Per serving (3/4 cup yogurt, 1/2 cup fruit,
    1 1/2 Tbsp nut mixture)
260 Cal, 13 g fat (saturated 3 g),
10 g protein, 25 g carbohydrate, 3 g fiber, 11 g sugar,
110 mg sodium

Equals: 1 Nutrisystem® Breakfast +
    1 Fruit + 1 Dairy/Protein

BUCKWHEAT PANCAKES WITH BERRIES SERVES 4

Buckwheat is not a cereal grain like wheat but is actually the seed of an annual that's related to sorrel and rhubarb. It has a nutty flavor and is ground into a gritty flour for making pancakes, muffins, cookies, cakes, Russian blinis and soba noodles.
Preparation time: 10 minutes Cooking time: 10–15 minutes

1 cup buckwheat flour
¼ cup stone-ground whole wheat flour
1½ teaspoons baking powder
2 tablespoons raw (Demerara) sugar
2 eggs, lightly beaten
1 cup buttermilk
1 teaspoon vanilla extract
olive oil spray
1½ cups low-fat natural yogurt
3 cups blueberries

1 Combine the flours, baking powder and sugar in a mixing bowl. Make a well in the center and pour in the eggs, buttermilk and vanilla extract and whisk until smooth. Add a little more milk if the pancake batter is too thick.

2 Heat a frying pan over medium heat and lightly spray with olive oil. Pour ¼ cup of the mixture into the pan and cook for 1–2 minutes each side, or until the pancake is golden and cooked. Repeat with the remaining mixture, to make 8 pancakes in total.

3 Serve two pancakes per person. Top pancakes with yogurt and blueberries.

 ACTIVITY TIP
Buy a pedometer and wear it on your waistband every day. Make it your goal to reach 10,000 steps on most days.

GI LOW Ⓖ
Per serving (2 pancakes, 6 oz yogurt, ³/₄ cup berries)
320 Cal, 5 g fat (saturated 2 g),
15 g protein, 53 g carbohydrate, 8 g fiber, 27 g sugar,
160 mg sodium

Equals: 1 Nutrisystem® Breakfast +
1 Fruit + 1 Dairy

ORANGE BIRCHER MUESLI SERVES 3

Soaking time: Overnight Preparation time: 5 minutes

1 cup rolled oats
¼ cup raisins
1 cup orange juice
1 apple, grated with skin on
2 tablespoons low-fat natural yogurt
¼ cup blueberries
4 strawberries, sliced

1 The night before, place the oats, raisins and orange juice in a bowl, cover and leave in the refrigerator overnight.

2 In the morning, add the grated apple and yogurt and mix well. Serve in two bowls topped with the blueberries and sliced strawberries.

GI LOW Ⓖ

Per serving (²/₃ cup)
250 Cal, 2.5 g fat (saturated .5 g),
6 g protein, 53 g carbohydrate, 6 g fiber, 20 g sugar,
20 mg sodium

Equals: 1 Nutrisystem® Breakfast + 1 Fruit

TOASTED MUESLI MAKES ABOUT 32 SERVINGS

Preparation time: 10 minutes Cooking time: 25–35 minutes

7½ cups rolled oats
2 cups rye or barley flakes (or use extra oats)
½ cup sesame seeds
1⅓ cups sliced almonds
1 cup wheat germ
1½ cups mixed dried fruit, such as peaches, pears, apricots, apples
2 cups raisins
½ cup pumpkin seeds
1 cup sunflower seeds

1 Preheat the oven to 350°F. Spread half the rolled oats and half the rye or barley flakes on a large ungreased baking tray. Bake for 10–15 minutes, stirring several times, until the oats are golden brown (take care they don't burn). Spread onto a large plate or tray to cool. Repeat with the remaining oats and rye or barley.

2 Put the sesame seeds and almonds on the tray and bake for 3 minutes, stirring occasionally, or until toasted and golden. Allow to cool.

3 Combine the toasted oats, rye, sesame seeds and almonds with the remaining ingredients and mix well. The toasted muesli will store for 1 month if kept in an airtight container.

GI LOW Ⓖ

Per 2 oz serving (4 Tbsp)
230 Cal, 9 g fat (saturated 1 g),
7 g protein, 32 g carbohydrate, 5 g fiber, 1 g sugar,
25 mg sodium

Equals: 1 Nutrisystem® Breakfast + 1 Fat

Recipe: Dr. Rosemary Stanton

MIXED BERRY MUFFINS MAKES 10

You will find unprocessed oat bran in the cereal section of your supermarket. It's soft and has quite a bland flavor but is very useful in baked goods, such as muffins, as a partial substitute for flour because it boosts the fiber and lowers the GI.

Soaking time: 10 minutes Preparation time: 10 minutes Cooking time: 15 minutes

½ cup All-Bran® cereal
½ cup low-fat milk
½ cup self-rising flour
2 teaspoons baking powder
½ teaspoon ground cinnamon
½ cup unprocessed oat bran
1 cup blueberries
1¼ cups raspberries
1 egg, lightly beaten
2 tablespoons pure floral honey
½ teaspoon vanilla extract

1 Preheat the oven to 350°F. Line a 12-cup muffin pan with paper baking cups.

2 Put the bran cereal in a bowl, pour over the milk and soak for 10 minutes. Sift the flour, baking powder and cinnamon into a large bowl. Stir in the oat bran, then fold in the blueberries and raspberries. Combine the egg, honey and vanilla in a small bowl.

3 Add the egg mixture and bran cereal mixture to the dry ingredients and stir gently with a wooden spoon until just combined; do not overmix. Spoon the mixture into the prepared muffin pan and bake for about 15 minutes, or until lightly browned and a wooden skewer inserted into the center of a muffin comes out clean. Cool for 5 minutes in the pan before transferring to a wire rack.

G GI LOW

Per muffin
80 Cal, 1 g fat (saturated 0 g),
3 g protein, 19 g carbohydrate, 2 g fiber, 6 g sugar,
100 mg sodium

Equals 1 Nutrisystem® Breakfast

FRUIT COMPOTE SERVES 6

We often sweeten recipes with honey rather than sugar. Since every species of flower has a unique nectar, honey from different types of flowers can have very different flavors and qualities. The lower GI honeys tend to be pure floral honeys rather than a commercially blended product. Preparation time: 10 minutes Cooking time: 10 minutes

3 cups apple juice
1 tablespoon pure floral honey
1 cinnamon stick
8 cardamom pods
³/₄ cup dried pear halves
1 ¼ cups dried apples
½ cup dried apricots
½ cup pitted prunes

1 Combine the apple juice, honey, cinnamon stick, cardamom pods, pears, apples and apricots in a saucepan. Bring to a boil, then reduce the heat and simmer for 10 minutes, or until the fruit has softened.

2 Remove the pan from the heat, add the prunes, then transfer to a serving dish and leave to cool. When cool, cover and refrigerate until ready to serve.

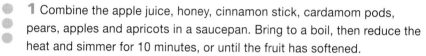 ACTIVITY TIP
People who exercise are happier—being active for just 20 minutes a day helps to lift your spirits and improve your mood.

GI LOW Ⓖ
Per serving (³/₄ cup)
210 Cal, 0 g fat (saturated 0 g),
1 g protein, 53 g carbohydrate, 3 g fiber, 40 g sugar,
105 mg sodium

Equals: 1 Nutrisystem® Breakfast + 1 Fruit

JULIE LE CLERC

MUSTARD-ROASTED FRUITS MAKES 4 CUPS, SERVES 12

These wonderful mustard-roasted fruits are like a hot, roasted, whole fruit chutney. All you need is a spoonful over a slice of lean ham off the bone, or serve with your favorite cold meats.

Preparation time: 10 minutes Cooking time: 30 minutes

1 cup dried figs
1 cup dried Mission figs
1 cup dried pear halves
½ cup dried apricots
½ cup pitted prunes
1 tablespoon mustard powder
2 tablespoons yellow mustard seeds
½ teaspoon salt
1 cup soft brown sugar
½ cup white wine vinegar
1½ cups dry white wine

1 Preheat the oven to 400°F. Place the dried fruit in a roasting pan, sprinkle over the mustard powder, mustard seeds, salt and sugar. Add the vinegar and wine and stir gently to combine.

2 Roast in the oven, stirring and tossing occasionally, for about 30 minutes, or until the fruits caramelize (check them after 20–25 minutes). Add extra liquid if you prefer them a little moister. The fruits are preserved in vinegar and sugar so will last for 2 weeks if stored, covered, in a clean jar or plastic container in the refrigerator.

● **GI LOW**
Per serving (⅓ cup)
170 Cal, 0 g fat (saturated 0 g),
1 g protein, 41 g carbohydrate, 2 g fiber, 23 g sugar,
210 mg sodium

Equals: 1 Nutrisystem® Breakfast
   (swap 1 fruit serving for a slice of bread)

Julie Le Clerc is the award-winning author of nine vibrant cookbooks. She was owner and chef of two successful cafés in New Zealand, had many years' experience in professional kitchens and boutique catering, worked as a private chef in homes around the world, and gained a reputation as an accomplished cooking demonstrator. These cooking experiences and a great love of travel continue to inspire and expand Julie's culinary repertoire. Returning to the Middle East for 3 months recently has increased her knowledge of, and affection for, the fascinating cuisine of these lands.

BERRY AND BANANA SMOOTHIE SERVES 2

Preparation time: 5 minutes

*½ cup frozen berries, such as
raspberries, strawberries,
blueberries, or a mixture
1 banana, sliced
1²/₃ cups evaporated skim milk
2 small scoops (¼ cup) low-fat frozen yogurt
or low-fat ice cream*

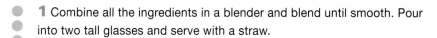

1 Combine all the ingredients in a blender and blend until smooth. Pour into two tall glasses and serve with a straw.

GI LOW ⓖ

Per serving (approximately 1½ cups)
260 Cal, 2 g fat (saturated 1 g),
17 g protein, 45 g carbohydrate, 2 g fiber, 36 g sugar,
230 mg sodium

Equals: 1 Nutrisystem® Breakfast + 1 Dairy/Protein + 1 Fruit

CARROT, APPLE AND GINGER JUICE SERVES 4

Preparation time: 10 minutes

*2 carrots, peeled
2 apples, cored
2¼ cups fresh orange juice
½ teaspoon finely grated ginger*

1 If you have a juicer, juice the carrots and apples into a small pitcher. Mix in the orange juice and ginger. Alternatively, use a blender to blend the ingredients until as smooth as possible. Pour the juice into four glasses and serve with ice, if desired.

COOK'S TIP

It's easy to overdo the calories when drinking fruit juice, so it is a good idea to mix a fruit with a vegetable, as we've done here. This cuts both the sweetness and the calories, while providing many of the nutrients found in whole food.

GI LOW ⓖ

Per serving (approximately 1½ cups)
120 Cal, 0 g fat (saturated 0 g),
1 g protein, 29 g carbohydrate, 3 g fiber, 23 g sugar,
25 mg sodium

Equals: 1 Nutrisystem® Breakfast

Left: Berry and banana smoothie

LUNCHES AND LIGHT MEALS

ALTHOUGH LUNCH IS OFTEN EATEN ON THE RUN, IT IS IMPORTANT TO REFUEL 4 OR 5 HOURS AFTER BREAKFAST. IT DOESN'T NEED TO BE A BIG MEAL. IN FACT, IF YOU FIND YOURSELF FEELING SLEEPY IN THE AFTERNOON, IT MAY HELP TO KEEP IT LIGHT WITH PROTEIN, VEGETABLES AND A SMALL SERVING OF CARBS.

BRUSCHETTA MAKES 4 OF EACH

Bruschetta, an Italian speciality, is toasted bread seasoned with olive oil and garlic. It is made using a dense, often day-old bread. Make the basic bruschetta and then choose from one of the toppings below. There is enough of each topping for four slices of bruschetta.
Preparation time: 10 minutes each Cooking time: 2–5 minutes each

BASIC BRUSCHETTA
4 slices sourdough bread, cut on the diagonal
olive oil spray
1 garlic clove, halved

TOMATO AND BASIL
3 vine-ripened tomatoes, finely chopped
1 garlic clove, minced
½ red onion, finely chopped
2 tablespoons finely shredded basil
2 teaspoons extra-virgin olive oil
2 teaspoons balsamic vinegar
freshly ground black pepper

RICOTTA AND ASPARAGUS
½ cup reduced fat ricotta cheese
1 tablespoon basil pesto
8 asparagus spears, trimmed
freshly ground black pepper

WHITE BEAN AND OLIVE
1 – 14 oz can white beans,
rinsed and drained
juice of ½ lemon
2 teaspoons olive oil
freshly ground black pepper
2 tablespoons chopped kalamata olives
4 thyme sprigs, to garnish

1 To make the basic bruschetta, spray the sourdough slices on both sides with olive oil and toast under a broiler until light golden brown. Rub the cut garlic cloves over each slice of toast.

2 To make the tomato and basil topping, combine the tomatoes, garlic, onion, basil, oil and balsamic vinegar in a bowl. Season with pepper, then spoon the tomato mixture onto the bruschetta.

3 To make the ricotta and asparagus topping, combine the ricotta cheese and pesto in a small bowl. Heat a grill or frying pan over medium heat, spray the asparagus with olive oil and cook for 2–3 minutes, or until tender. Cut the asparagus into pieces. Spread the bruschetta with the ricotta mixture, top with asparagus pieces and season with pepper.

4 To make the white bean and olive topping, put the beans, lemon juice and oil in the bowl of a food processor, season with pepper, then blend to a smooth purée—adding more lemon juice for a creamier texture, if desired. Spread the bean mixture over the bruschetta, top with the olives and garnish with a sprig of thyme.

Ⓖ GI LOW
Per slice (tomato and basil)
110 Cal, 3 g fat (saturated 0 g),
4 g protein, 16 g carbohydrate,
    1 g fiber, 3 g sugar,
160 mg sodium

Equals: 1 Nutrisystem® Lunch

Ⓖ GI LOW
Per slice (ricotta and asparagus)
120 Cal, 3 g fat (saturated 1 g),
7 g protein, 17 g carbohydrate,
    2 g fiber, 3 g sugar,
220 mg sodium

Equals: 1 Nutrisystem® Lunch

Ⓖ GI LOW
Per slice (white bean and olive)
170 Cal, 5 g fat (saturated .5 g),
8 g protein, 28 g carbohydrate,
    5 g fiber, 1 g sugar,
580 mg sodium

Equals: 1 Nutrisystem® Lunch

CRUMBED CHICKEN ON ROAST SWEET POTATO SALAD SERVES 3

Crumbed pieces of tender chicken, layered on a tasty sweet potato salad and drizzled with a creamy honey mustard dressing—the perfect dish for a lunch or light meal. Preparation time: 20 minutes Cooking time: 25 minutes

ROAST SWEET POTATO SALAD
1 tablespoon olive oil
2 tablespoons balsamic vinegar
3 teaspoons soft brown sugar
1 orange sweet potato (about 10½ oz),
cut into ¼ in thick slices
6 cups mixed green salad leaves
1 tablespoon chopped basil, to garnish

CRUMBED CHICKEN
2 tablespoons low-fat natural yogurt
2 tablespoons low-fat milk
1 cup dry whole grain
breadcrumbs (see tip)
½ teaspoon paprika
freshly ground black pepper
10½ oz skinless chicken breast or
thigh fillets, trimmed and cut in half

HONEY MUSTARD DRESSING
1 tablespoon Dijon mustard
1 tablespoon ketchup
2 teaspoons lemon juice
2 tablespoons low-fat natural yogurt
1 teaspoon pure floral honey

1 Preheat the oven to 425°F. To make the roast sweet potato salad, combine the oil, vinegar and brown sugar in a large bowl. Add the sweet potato and toss to coat in the oil. Transfer to a shallow baking tray and bake for 25 minutes, or until soft and starting to brown. Remove from the oven and leave for 10 minutes to cool a little. (Note: If you prepare the sweet potato and the crumbed chicken at the same time, they can then go in the oven together.)

2 To make the crumbed chicken, put the yogurt in a flat dish or bowl and stir in the milk to thin it a little. Combine the breadcrumbs and paprika in a bowl and season with pepper. Dip the chicken into the yogurt, allow the excess to drain off, then coat in the breadcrumbs. Put the crumbed chicken on a baking tray lined with parchment paper and bake for 20 minutes, or until the chicken is golden brown and cooked through. Remove and slice into strips on the diagonal.

3 To make the honey mustard dressing, put all the ingredients into a small bowl and stir to combine.

4 To serve, lay the salad leaves on a plate, top with slices of roasted sweet potato, a few more salad leaves, then more sweet potato. Lay the crumbed chicken on top of the salad and drizzle with the honey mustard dressing. Scatter over the basil.

COOK'S TIP
To make the dry whole grain breadcrumbs, take 4 slices of a low GI whole grain bread and break into small pieces. Spread out on a baking tray and bake in a 425°F oven for 5 minutes, or until golden brown. Cool slightly, then transfer to the bowl of a food processor and process to make small crumbs.

GI LOW G
Per serving (2 oz chicken, 2 cups greens,
⅓ cup sweet potato, 1 Tbsp dressing)
395 Cal, 8 g fat (saturated 1.5 g),
32 g protein, 50 g carbohydrate, 6 g fiber, 17 g sugar,
585 mg sodium

Equals: 1 Nutrisystem® Lunch +
2 Vegetables + 1 Protein

QUINOA TABBOULI WITH SHRIMP SERVES 6

Quinoa is one of those versatile grains that you can make a meal of throughout the day—and it has a low GI of 53. This version of tabbouli uses quinoa instead of bulgur wheat and is made with pistachios. The fresh, strong flavors of lime and basil complement the shrimp beautifully. Marinating time: 30 minutes Preparation time: 15 minutes Cooking time: 15 minutes

24 large shrimp, raw, peeled and deveined,
with tails intact
zest and juice of 1 lemon
1 teaspoon ground cumin
2 jalapeño peppers, finely chopped
½ cup low-fat natural yogurt, to serve

PISTACHIO TABBOULI
1 cup quinoa, rinsed well
1 tablespoon olive oil
1 teaspoon ground cumin
freshly ground black pepper
½ cup pistachio nuts,
roughly chopped
½ red onion, finely chopped
1 tomato, chopped
½ cup chopped basil
juice of 1 lime

1 Put the shrimp, lemon zest and juice, cumin and jalapeños in a non-metallic bowl. Mix well to coat the shrimp in the marinade. Refrigerate the shrimp for 30 minutes to allow the flavors to develop.

2 To make the pistachio tabbouli, put the rinsed quinoa in a saucepan and cover with 2 cups water. Bring to a boil, then reduce the heat and simmer for about 10 minutes, or until the grains are tender and translucent. While still warm, transfer to a bowl and add the remaining ingredients. Mix well and set aside.

3 Soak 6 bamboo skewers for 30 minutes. Thread 4 shrimp onto each skewer and cook on a grill or under a broiler for 2 minutes on each side, or until pink and cooked through. Spoon the tabbouli onto plates, top with one skewer per plate, and drizzle with the yogurt.

COOK'S TIP
As a variation, use almonds or cashews instead of the pistachio nuts, or substitute mint leaves for the basil.

G GI LOW

Per serving (4 shrimp, ½ cup quinoa)
260 Cal, 11 g fat (saturated 1 g),
14 g protein, 26 g carbohydrate, 9 g fiber, 4 g sugar,
140 mg sodium

Equals: 1 Nutrisystem® Lunch + 1 Protein

LENTIL BRUSCHETTA SERVES 16

This red lentil spread makes a delicious topping for bruschetta, or you could use it as a sandwich spread or a dip for fresh vegetables. Serve with a green salad, if desired.

Preparation time: 15 minutes Cooking time: 20 minutes

1 cup red lentils
1 bay leaf
3 tablespoons olive oil
1 garlic clove, minced
1 large red pepper, finely chopped
1 tablespoon paprika
1 loaf (1 lb 7 oz) sliced sourdough bread (about 16 slices)
½ cup grated strong cheese, such as Romano

1 Rinse the lentils and place them in a large saucepan. Cover with plenty of water and add the bay leaf. Bring to a boil, then reduce the heat and simmer for about 15 minutes, or until the lentils are very soft, skimming off any foam as they cook. Drain and remove the bay leaf.

2 Heat the oil in a frying pan and sauté the garlic and pepper for about 5 minutes, or until soft. Stir in the paprika, then remove from the heat. Mix in the lentils. (For a smooth spread, purée the mixture in a food processor.)

3 Spread the lentils onto slices of toasted sourdough, sprinkle with the cheese and place under a broiler until the cheese has melted. Serve immediately.

ACTIVITY TIP
Use half an hour of your lunch break to get outside and take a walk. This is an easy way to fit regular exercise into a busy work schedule.

GI LOW

Per serving (1 slice bruschetta with 2 Tbsp lentil spread)
190 Cal, 5 g fat (saturated 1 g),
8 g protein, 26 g carbohydrate, 4 g fiber, 3 g sugar,
250 mg sodium

Equals: 1 Nutrisystem® Lunch

Recipe from: Passion for Pulses

CHACHOUKA SERVES 4

Chachouka, eggs served in a tangy mixture of tomatoes, peppers—red, yellow and green—and chiles, is enjoyed throughout the Middle East. Serve as a brunch or light meal with chunky grainy toast.

Preparation time: 15 minutes Cooking time: 25–35 minutes

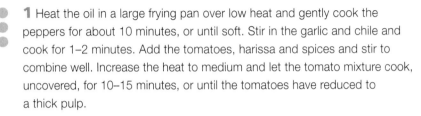

*1 tablespoon olive oil
1 small red pepper, seeded and thinly sliced
1 small yellow pepper, seeded and thinly sliced
1 small green pepper, seeded and thinly sliced
2 garlic cloves, minced
1–2 small red chiles, seeded and finely chopped
1 – 14 oz can Italian peeled tomatoes, chopped
1 teaspoon harissa (page 134, or prepared)
1 teaspoon caraway seeds, ground
1/2 teaspoon sweet paprika
1/2 teaspoon ground cumin
4 large eggs
2 tablespoons chopped chives or flat-leaf parsley
4 thick slices grainy bread*

1 Heat the oil in a large frying pan over low heat and gently cook the peppers for about 10 minutes, or until soft. Stir in the garlic and chile and cook for 1–2 minutes. Add the tomatoes, harissa and spices and stir to combine well. Increase the heat to medium and let the tomato mixture cook, uncovered, for 10–15 minutes, or until the tomatoes have reduced to a thick pulp.

2 Using the back of a spoon, make four equally spaced depressions in the tomato mixture, then carefully break one egg into each depression. Cover and leave to simmer for about 5 minutes, or until the whites are just cooked but the yolks are still soft. Sprinkle with the chives or parsley and serve immediately with toasted grainy bread.

3 As an alternative cooking method, pour the tomato mixture into four individual ovenproof dishes. Make a slight depression in the top of the tomato mixture in each dish, then break one egg into each depression. Cover lightly with foil and bake in a preheated 350°F oven for 15–20 minutes, or until the eggs are set. Take care when serving, as the dishes will be hot.

G GI LOW

Per serving (1 cup vegetable mixture, 1 egg, 1 slice bread)
260 Cal, 13 g fat (saturated 3 g),
12 g protein, 24 g carbohydrate, 5 g fiber, 8 g sugar,
410 mg sodium

Equals: 1 Nutrisystem® Lunch + 1 Protein

Recipe: Liz and Ian Hemphill, Herbies Spices

MARGARET FULTON

VEGETABLE CHILI BOWL SERVES 6

This vegetable variation of chili con carne has a lively spicy taste and is a complete meal in itself. Vegetarians will love this chunky chili dish and meat eaters won't even notice that the meat is missing.

Preparation time: 15 minutes Cooking time: 20 minutes

2 tablespoons olive oil
2 onions, roughly chopped
3 garlic cloves, minced
2 red peppers, halved and cut
into squares
2 zucchini
1 tablespoon chili powder, or to taste
1 tablespoon ground cumin
2 – 14 oz cans peeled tomatoes,
roughly chopped, juice reserved
1 – 15½ oz can red kidney beans,
rinsed and drained
1 – 15½ oz can chickpeas,
rinsed and drained
¼ teaspoon salt
freshly ground black pepper
½ cup chopped flat-leaf parsley
½ cup chopped cilantro leaves
2 tablespoons lemon juice

1 Heat the oil in a 4-quart Dutch oven over medium heat. Add the onions, garlic and peppers and cook for 5 minutes, then add the zucchini and cook for 3 minutes.

2 Add the chili powder and cumin and stir for a minute to combine, then add the chopped tomatoes with their juice, the drained kidney beans and chickpeas. Season with the salt and plenty of pepper. Cover and cook over low heat for 8–10 minutes, or until the zucchini is tender. Stir in the parsley, cilantro and lemon juice.

3 If preferred, you may like to serve this with separate bowls of grated cheddar cheese and yogurt for everyone to help themselves, plus some crusty low GI bread, such as sourdough, to mop up the juices.

Margaret Fulton is one of Australia's leading food writers. Through her interest in food and nutrition, Margaret is a Governor (Honorary) of the University of Sydney Nutrition Research Foundation. Concerned for our future food supplies, Margaret has taken a stand against genetically modified food. She launched the *True Food Guide*, a Greenpeace book that advises shoppers on GE-free foods. Her pre-eminence in the food world was given official recognition when she was awarded the OAM (Medal of the Order of Australia) in the Queen's Birthday Honours of 1993. Margaret was made a National Living Treasure in 1998.

GI LOW Ⓖ
Per serving (¹/₆ recipe)
160 Cal, 5 g fat (saturated .5 g),
8 g protein, 23 g carbohydrate,
9 g fiber, 8 g sugar,
170 mg sodium

**Equals: 1 Nutrisystem® Lunch +
1 Vegetable**

POTATO AND SWEET CORN FRITTATA SERVES 4

Frittata is one of the easiest meals to prepare when you want to make do with what's in the pantry and refrigerator. Virtually any combination of vegetables is possible. Here we use new potatoes, onion and sweet corn, but peas and a little bacon are nice additions, if preferred. Preparation time: 20 minutes Cooking time: 20 minutes

1 tablespoon olive oil
1 onion, chopped
1 garlic clove, minced
1 – 15½ oz can new potatoes, drained and cubed
1 – 11 oz can sweet corn kernels, drained
6 eggs
⅓ cup low-fat milk
1 tablespoon chopped parsley
freshly ground black pepper

VEGETABLE SALAD
3 cups sugar snap peas or snow peas, trimmed
12 asparagus spears, trimmed, cut into 1¼ in lengths
2½ cups broccoli, broken into small florets
2 tablespoons lemon juice
1 tablespoon olive oil

1 Heat half the oil in a large non-stick frying pan (with heatproof handle) over medium heat. Add the onion and garlic and cook for 3 minutes, or until the onion is translucent. Add the potatoes and corn kernels to the pan and cook for 1–2 minutes to heat through, then transfer the vegetables to a bowl.

2 Break the eggs into another bowl, add the milk and parsley, season with pepper and beat lightly with a fork until combined.

3 Add the remaining oil to the frying pan, swirling the oil around to coat the base of the pan. Add the vegetables to the pan, spreading them out, then pour the egg mixture evenly over the vegetables. Cover and cook over medium-low heat for 10 minutes, or until the egg mixture is partially set. Place under a broiler until the frittata is golden brown and puffed on top.

4 To make the vegetable salad, bring a large saucepan of water to a boil. Add the snap peas, asparagus and broccoli and boil for 2–3 minutes, or until the vegetables are bright green and just tender. Drain, rinse under cold water and refrigerate.

5 To make a salad dressing, put the lemon juice and oil in a screw-top jar and shake to combine. Serve the frittata in wedges with the salad and drizzle with the dressing.

G GI LOW
Per serving (¼ frittata with 1 cup vegetable salad)
320 Cal, 15 g fat (saturated 3.5 g),
15 g protein, 30 g carbohydrate, 6 g fiber, 8 g sugar,
580 mg sodium

Equals: 1 Nutrisystem® Lunch + 1 Protein

BEEFBURGERS WITH SALSA SERVES 4

Most burgers are made using ground hamburger, which is quite fatty (the fat makes them moist). Using ground rump steak with all the fat trimmed off (ask your butcher to grind it for you) may make this burger a little drier, but with the delicious tomato and bean salsa you won't notice the difference. Preparation time: 15 minutes Cooking time: 1 hour 10 minutes

1 lb 2 oz lean ground beef
½ onion, finely chopped
½ cup flat-leaf parsley,
finely chopped
freshly ground black pepper
1 tablespoon olive oil

TOMATO AND BEAN SALSA
1 tablespoon olive oil
1 small onion, finely chopped
1 small red chile, seeded and finely chopped
3 garlic cloves, minced
1 teaspoon ground cumin
½ teaspoon sweet paprika
2 – 14 oz cans plum tomatoes
1 – 14 oz can red kidney beans, drained
3 tablespoons chopped flat-leaf parsley

1 To make the tomato and bean salsa, heat the oil in a saucepan over medium heat, then add the onion and chile and cook for 5 minutes, or until the onion is soft. Add the garlic, cumin and paprika and cook for 2 minutes. Break the tomatoes into chunks in a bowl, then add them to the pan. Bring to a boil, then reduce the heat and simmer for 30 minutes. Add the kidney beans, return to a boil, then reduce the heat and simmer for 20 minutes. Stir in the parsley.

2 To make the burgers, combine the ground beef with the onion and parsley and season with pepper. Shape the mixture into four flat rounds, pressing firmly into shape. Brush each with a little oil, then cook on a grill or in a frying pan for 3–6 minutes on each side, turning once, until golden brown and cooked through. Serve the beefburgers with the salsa, and with a green salad, if desired.

GI LOW Ⓖ
Per serving (1 burger and ½ cup salsa)
350 Cal, 12 g fat (saturated 2.5 g),
33 g protein, 27 g carbohydrate, 11 g fiber, 9 g sugar,
360 mg sodium

Equals 1 Nutrisystem® Lunch + 2 Vegetables + 1 Protein

Recipe: Judy Davie, The Food Coach

PARSLEY, BUTTER BEAN AND CHERRY TOMATO STEW SERVES 4

This quick and easy stew makes a simple side dish to serve with meat or chicken, or enjoy as a light meal in itself. Top with pitted black olives if you wish. Preparation time: 20 minutes Cooking time: 15 minutes

1 tablespoon olive oil
1 red onion, chopped
1 red pepper, thinly sliced
1 yellow pepper, thinly sliced
2 garlic cloves, minced (or more to taste)
1 in piece ginger, grated
pinch of saffron threads
20 cherry tomatoes, halved
½ teaspoon sugar
2 – 14 oz cans butter beans, rinsed and drained
½ teaspoon ground cinnamon
1 teaspoon paprika
freshly ground black pepper
½ small bunch flat-leaf parsley, roughly chopped
2 whole grain pitas, warmed and sliced

1 Heat the oil in a large frying pan over medium heat. Add the onion, peppers, garlic and ginger and cook for 10 minutes, or until the onions are golden and soft. Stir in the saffron threads, then the tomatoes and sugar and cook for 5 minutes.

2 When the tomatoes are heated through, add the butter beans, cinnamon and paprika. Stir gently. Season with pepper and sprinkle over the parsley. Serve with pita bread for mopping up the juices, if desired.

ACTIVITY TIP
Gardening and do-it-yourself repairs are great ways to be more active at home when weather permits. Otherwise, do some spring cleaning around the house for a total body workout.

G GI LOW
Per serving (1½ cups stew and ½ pita)
200 Cal, 4 g fat (saturated .5 g),
12 g protein, 41 g carbohydrate, 11 g fiber, 8 g sugar,
500 mg sodium

Equals: 1 Nutrisystem® Lunch

CHERMOULA CHICKPEA BURGERS SERVES 4

Chermoula gives these chickpea burgers a tangy Moroccan flavor. Chermoula combines the robust flavors of cumin, paprika and turmeric with onion, parsley and coriander, plus a hint of garlic and cayenne pepper.

Preparation time: 20 minutes Marinating time: 20 minutes Cooking time: 15 minutes

CHICKPEA BURGERS
1 tablespoon extra-virgin olive oil
1 large onion, finely chopped
1 garlic clove, minced
1 – 14 oz can chickpeas,
rinsed and drained
1 cup loosely packed fresh
whole grain breadcrumbs
1 egg, lightly beaten
freshly ground black pepper
1–2 tablespoons chickpea flour,
to thicken (optional)
2 tablespoons chermoula spice mix
(page 134, or prepared)
1 teaspoon olive oil

SERVING SUGGESTIONS
pita bread, warmed and cut into quarters
lettuce leaves
hummus (page 135, or ready-to-serve)
tabbouli (page 135, or ready-to-serve)

1 To make the chickpea burgers, heat the oil in a frying pan, add the onion and garlic and cook over low heat for 5 minutes, or until golden. Put the chickpeas in a food processor and purée until they resemble breadcrumbs. Add the fresh breadcrumbs and egg and season with pepper, then add the onion and garlic and process for a few seconds, or until the ingredients are just combined. Add 1–2 tablespoons chickpea flour if the mixture is too wet.

2 Use 1 heaping tablespoon of the mixture to form each burger (the mixture will make 8 burgers in total). Mix the chermoula with 2 tablespoons water. Brush the burgers generously with the chermoula, then leave to marinate for 20 minutes or so.

3 Heat the olive oil in a non-stick frying pan or on a griddle and cook the chickpea burgers over medium heat for 4–5 minutes each side, or until browned. Don't have the heat too high or they will burn, which will spoil the flavor.

4 Serve the chickpea burgers with pita bread and lettuce leaves and separate bowls of hummus and tabbouli, and assemble the burgers at the table.

GI LOW **G**

Per serving (2 burgers)
290 Cal, 8 g fat (saturated 1.5 g),
10 g protein, 45 g carbohydrate, 6 g fiber, 4 g sugar,
510 mg sodium

Equals: 1 Nutrisystem® Lunch + 1 Protein

SWEET POTATO CAKES WITH ROAST TOMATO SALAD SERVES 4

Don't hold back on the tomato salad with your sweet potato cakes. Tomatoes are an almost exclusive source of the antioxidant lycopene, associated with a reduced risk of some cancers. Preparation time: 25 minutes Cooking time: 45 minutes

SWEET POTATO CAKES
1 large potato (10½ oz),
roughly chopped
1 orange sweet potato (10½ oz),
roughly chopped
olive oil spray
2 slices bacon, fat trimmed, chopped
1 cup rolled oats
2 tablespoons chopped parsley
freshly ground black pepper

ROAST TOMATO SALAD
3 plum tomatoes, halved lengthways
1 garlic clove, minced
2 teaspoons olive oil
freshly ground black pepper
11½ oz baby spinach leaves

HERB MAYONNAISE
1 tablespoon mayonnaise
1 tablespoon low-fat natural yogurt
2 teaspoons finely chopped chives
1 tablespoon shredded basil

1 Preheat the oven to 400°F. To make the roast tomato salad, place the tomatoes, cut-side up, on a baking tray. Smear the cut side of the tomatoes with the garlic, drizzle over the oil and season with pepper. Bake for 30 minutes, or until soft.

2 Meanwhile, to make the sweet potato cakes, cook the potato and sweet potato in a large saucepan of boiling water for 10 minutes, or until soft.

3 Spray a non-stick frying pan with olive oil and cook the bacon over medium heat until browned. Put the oats into the bowl of a food processor and process briefly until the oats resemble coarse breadcrumbs.

4 Drain the cooked potato and sweet potato and mash them. Add the bacon, oats and parsley and season with pepper. When cool enough to handle, shape the potato mixture into four patties.

5 Reheat the frying pan over medium heat, spray with olive oil and cook the sweet potato cakes for 2–3 minutes on each side, or until browned.

6 To make the herb mayonnaise, combine all the ingredients in a bowl.

7 To serve, place two sweet potato cakes on each plate and top with a few spinach leaves, three tomato halves and a dollop of mayonnaise.

G GI LOW

Per serving (1 potato patty, 2 cups salad, 1 Tbsp herb mayo)
230 Cal, 6 g fat (saturated 1 g),
8 g protein, 38 g carbohydrate, 8 g fiber, 4 g sugar,
220 mg sodium

Equals: 1 Nutrisystem® Lunch + 2 Vegetables

TUSCAN-STYLE BEANS WITH TOMATOES AND SAGE SERVES 4

Tuscan beans can be served as a course on their own—either hot or cold—or as an accompaniment to meat dishes. Provide plenty of crusty sourdough bread to mop up the juices. Preparation time: 15 minutes Cooking time: 25 minutes

1 cup shelled fresh (or frozen)
fava beans
2 teaspoons extra-virgin olive oil
2 garlic cloves, minced
1 – 14 oz can Italian peeled tomatoes,
chopped
1 – 14 oz can cannellini beans,
rinsed and drained
1½ teaspoons finely chopped sage
or ½ teaspoon dried sage
freshly ground black pepper

1 Bring a saucepan of water to a boil and blanch the beans in boiling water for 3 minutes. Drain and refresh under cold running water. Peel the outer skins from the beans when they are cool enough to handle.

2 Heat the oil in a saucepan over low heat and cook the garlic for about 2 minutes. Add the tomatoes, cannellini beans and sage and simmer, covered, for 10 minutes. Stir in the fava beans and cook gently for 5–10 minutes, or until tender. Season with pepper.

COOK'S TIP
Sage has a lovely fresh aroma and flavor but it is quite intense. Use only 2 or 3 leaves so as not to overpower the other flavors in the dish. Dried sage (and dried herbs in general) has a more intense, concentrated flavor than fresh sage, so you only need to use about half the amount.

GI LOW G

Per serving (1 cup)
250 Cal, 3.5 g fat (saturated 0 g),
15 g protein, 42 g carbohydrate, 14 g fiber, 9 g sugar,
250 mg sodium

Equals: 1 Nutrisystem® Lunch + 1 Protein

NASI GORENG SERVES 4

Nasi goreng—Indonesian-style fried rice—is great as a light lunch using leftover cooked rice from the night before. Make sure you use one of the lower GI rices such as basmati, brown or wild rice. Uncle Ben's converted long grain rice is also a good choice.
Preparation time: 10 minutes Cooking time: 10–15 minutes

4 eggs, at room temperature
1 egg, lightly beaten
1 teaspoon peanut oil
1 large onion, finely chopped
2 garlic cloves, minced
1 tablespoon grated ginger
4 cups cooked basmati rice
1 tablespoon oyster sauce
2 tablespoons reduced sodium soy sauce
chopped parsley or scallions, to serve

1 Bring a large saucepan or deep frying pan of water to a simmer and carefully crack the eggs and gently slip them, one at a time, into the simmering water. Poach for 3–4 minutes, or until the eggs are cooked to your liking. Lift out with a slotted spoon and drain on paper towels.

2 Heat a non-stick frying pan over medium heat, add the beaten egg and stir-fry until the egg is scrambled. Remove and set aside.

3 Heat the oil in the pan, add the onion, garlic and ginger and lightly fry for 3–5 minutes, or until the onion is soft. Add the cooked rice and toss well. Pour in the oyster sauce and soy sauce and toss to coat the rice in the sauces. Stir in the scrambled egg.

4 Spoon the rice into four bowls or plates and top each with a poached egg. Sprinkle with chopped parsley or scallions.

COOK'S TIPS
To obtain 4 cups cooked rice you will need 1 1/3 cups raw rice.

The GI of rice varies according to the variety and its proportion of the slower digested amylose starch.

G GI MEDIUM
Per serving (1 egg, 3/4 cup rice mixture)
380 Cal, 8 g fat (saturated 2 g),
14 g protein, 64 g carbohydrate, 3 g fiber, 2 g sugar,
400 mg sodium

Equals: 1 Nutrisystem® Lunch + 2 Protein

Recipe: Jill McMillan

SUSHI ROLLS MAKES 4 ROLLS

The low GI of sushi rolls is due to the special Japanese rice called koshihikari and the addition of rice vinegar. Add to this the nutrient-rich fish and you have a perfect light lunch that will keep the hunger pangs at bay all afternoon.

Preparation time: 20 minutes Standing time: 10 minutes Cooking time: 15 minutes

1 cup sushi rice (koshihikari rice)
¼ cup Japanese rice vinegar
1 tablespoon sugar
4 sheets nori, toasted

SALMON FILLING
1¾ oz smoked salmon, sliced
½ avocado, thinly sliced

TUNA FILLING
1 – 3½ oz can tuna in water, drained
1 tablespoon low-fat mayonnaise
½ small cucumber, seeds removed,
cut into long strips

1 Cook the rice in a large saucepan of boiling water for 13–15 minutes, or until the rice is tender. Drain the rice, without rinsing it, and place in a large bowl. Add the rice vinegar and sugar and stir into the rice. Cover with plastic wrap and leave to cool for about 10 minutes.

2 Run a bamboo sushi mat under water and shake off the excess water. Place one nori sheet on the sushi mat, rough-side up and with the long end of the sheet closest to you. Using wet hands, place a quarter of the rice on the nori sheet, pat down the rice to cover the sheet, leaving 1½ in at the top of the sheet. Press the rice firmly onto the sheet and make a slight indent in the rice 1½ in from the bottom of the sheet, closest to you.

3 To make the salmon-filled rolls, place half the smoked salmon and half the avocado in the indent along the rice. Using the bamboo mat, firmly roll up the sushi. Remove the mat. Using a wet knife, cut the roll into thick slices. Repeat to make the second roll.

4 To make the tuna-filled rolls, combine the tuna with the mayonnaise. Place half the cucumber strips and half the tuna in the indent along the rice and roll up the sushi. Repeat to make the second roll.

5 You may like to serve the sushi rolls with accompaniments such as soy sauce for dipping (mix a little wasabi into the soy sauce for extra flavor) and pickled ginger.

GI LOW Ⓖ
Per salmon roll (1 roll)
230 Cal, 4 g fat (saturated .5 g),
6 g protein, 44 g carbohydrate,
3 g fiber, 2 g sugar,
100 mg sodium

Equals: 1 Nutrisystem® Lunch + 1 Fat

GI LOW Ⓖ
Per tuna roll (1 roll)
220 Cal, 1 g fat (saturated 0 g),
10 g protein, 43 g carbohydrate,
1 g fiber, 3 g sugar,
40 mg sodium

Equals: 1 Nutrisystem® Lunch + 1 Fat

SOUPS AND SALADS

SOUPS AND SALADS MAKE GREAT STARTERS,
ESPECIALLY WHEN YOU WANT TO LOSE WEIGHT.
THE EVIDENCE IS IN—WE KNOW THAT EATING
A MIXED SALAD TOSSED IN A VINAIGRETTE
DRESSING OR SIPPING A BOWL OF VEGETABLE
SOUP BEFORE A MAIN MEAL WILL HELP TO FILL
YOU UP SO THAT YOU WILL EAT LESS OVERALL.

MINESTRONE SERVES 4

Minestrone is absolutely delicious as a warming, hearty winter meal. And it is worth the little extra effort and time it takes to make as this quantity will generously serve four for a main meal or six as a starter and still leave leftovers for lunch. Leave out the bacon if you want a vegetarian meal. Preparation time: 20 minutes Cooking time: 50–55 minutes

1 tablespoon olive oil
1 large onion, finely chopped
1 leek, thinly sliced
2 garlic cloves, minced
2 carrots, sliced into 1/4 in rounds,
or finely chopped
2 celery sticks, thinly sliced
1 – 14 oz can Italian peeled tomatoes,
chopped
1 bay leaf
6 cups reduced sodium chicken,
beef or vegetable stock
1/2 cup small pasta or pasta pieces
1 – 14 oz can cannellini beans,
rinsed and drained
1 cup fresh or frozen peas
1 cup finely shredded cabbage
freshly ground black pepper
basil pesto or sun-dried tomato pesto,
to serve (optional)
shaved Parmesan cheese, to serve (optional)

1 Heat the oil in a large heavy-based soup saucepan over medium heat. Add the onion, leek and garlic and cook for about 5 minutes, or until the onion is golden and soft. Add the carrots, celery, tomatoes and bay leaf. Pour in 5 cups of the stock and bring to a boil, then reduce the heat and simmer, covered, for 30 minutes.

2 Stir in the pasta and continue to simmer for 10–15 minutes, or until the pasta is al dente. Add more stock if the mixture is too thick.

3 Add the beans, peas and cabbage, season with pepper, then stir to combine and cook for a few minutes to heat the vegetables through.

4 Serve with a dollop of basil or sun-dried tomato pesto and scatter over the Parmesan cheese, if using. You may like to serve with sourdough bread to mop up the juices.

COOK'S TIP
To freeze, cool the soup to room temperature and divide among single serve plastic containers with lids. Label with the recipe name and date using an indelible marker.

G GI LOW

Per serving (2 1/2 cups)
310 Cal, 2.5 g fat (saturated 0 g),
15 g protein, 57 g carbohydrate, 11 g fiber, 11 g sugar,
400 mg sodium

Equals: 1 Nutrisystem® Lunch + 1 Vegetable + 1 Protein

PAN-FRIED LAMB SALAD WITH TZATZIKI SERVES 4

Tzatziki is a traditional Greek cucumber and yogurt dip and makes a delicious dressing for this lamb salad. It is often served as a dip with grape leaves, or vegetable platters. You can find prepared tzatziki in the refrigerated section of the supermarket.

Preparation time: 20 minutes   Cooking time: 10 minutes

olive oil spray
1 lb 2 oz lamb fillets
freshly ground black pepper
2 cups arugula leaves
2 cups baby spinach leaves
1 cup cherry tomatoes, halved
1/2 cucumber, sliced
1/2 cup peas, cooked al dente
1/2 red onion, thinly sliced
1 red pepper, thinly sliced
2 tablespoons olive oil
juice of 1/2 lemon

TZATZIKI
1/2 cucumber
1 cup low-fat natural yogurt
1 garlic clove, minced
juice of 1/2 lemon
1 tablespoon chopped mint

1 To make the tzatziki, grate the cucumber into a bowl. Wrap the cucumber flesh in a tea towel and squeeze out the water. Mix the cucumber with the remaining tzatziki ingredients.

2 Heat a non-stick frying pan over medium heat and spray with a little olive oil. Season the lamb with pepper and cook for 3 minutes on each side—the meat should still be pink in the middle. Remove from the pan and allow to rest for a few minutes before slicing.

3 Meanwhile, mix together the arugula, spinach, tomatoes, cucumber, peas, onion and pepper in a bowl.

4 Make a dressing by combining the oil and lemon juice in a screw-top jar, season with pepper and shake well. Drizzle the dressing over the salad, then divide the salad between four plates. Lay the lamb fillets over the salad and top with a generous spoonful of tzatziki.

GI LOW Ⓖ

Per serving (3 oz lamb, 2 cups salad, 1 Tbsp tzatziki)
350 Cal, 15 g fat (saturated 4 g),
35 g protein, 21 g carbohydrate, 6 g fiber, 12 g sugar,
190 mg sodium

Equals: 1 Nutrisystem® Lunch + 2 Vegetables + 1 Protein

WARM VEGETABLE SALAD SERVES 2

This salad makes it easy to boost your vegetable intake—something we are all being urged to do. The lemon yogurt dressing is delicious with all sorts of vegetables, so try it with zucchini, sweet potato or pumpkin, for a change.

Preparation time: 10 minutes Cooking time: 3 minutes

1 large carrot, sliced
4 cauliflower florets, broken into small pieces
4 broccoli florets, broken into small pieces
20 green beans, trimmed and halved
2 tablespoons chopped flat-leaf parsley

LEMON YOGURT DRESSING
2 tablespoons low-fat natural yogurt
2 tablespoons lemon juice
2 teaspoons pure floral honey
1 teaspoon crushed garlic
freshly ground black pepper

1 To blanch the vegetables, bring a saucepan of water to a boil. Add the carrot and cauliflower and cook for 2 minutes. Add the broccoli and beans and cook for 1 minute, or until crisp-tender.

2 Meanwhile, make the lemon yogurt dressing. Combine all the ingredients in a screw-top jar and shake to combine.

3 Drain the vegetables and refresh briefly under cold water. Pat dry, then place the vegetables in a bowl and pour over the dressing, tossing to coat. Sprinkle with parsley and serve.

ACTIVITY TIP
Be an active role model for your family—if you exercise, your partner and children are more likely to.

G GI LOW

Per serving (¹/₂ recipe with 1 Tbsp dressing)
130 Cal, 0 fat (saturated 0 g),
4 g protein, 31 g carbohydrate, 4 g fiber, 21 g sugar,
50 mg sodium

Equals: 2 Vegetable + 1 Fat

SWEET AND SOUR CHICKEN SALAD SERVES 3

Bulgur wheat is a versatile low GI cereal grain made from hard durum wheat that has been steamed, cracked and dried. It is also known as cracked wheat. Use it in tabbouli or add to pilafs, vegetable burgers, stuffings, stews and even soups.
Preparation time: 20 minutes Cooking time: 15 minutes

12 green beans, trimmed
8 thin asparagus spears, trimmed
12 snow peas
1³/₄ cups cooked chicken, shredded or sliced
2 cups baby spinach or arugula leaves

SWEET AND SOUR DRESSING
1 tablespoon white wine vinegar
1 tablespoon extra-virgin olive oil
2 teaspoons finely chopped lemon, with juice
2 teaspoons raw (Demerara) sugar
freshly ground black pepper

MINTED BULGUR WHEAT
¹/₂ cup bulgur wheat
¹/₂ cup boiling water
2 tablespoons finely chopped mint

1 To blanch the vegetables, bring a saucepan of water to a boil. Put the beans, asparagus and snow peas in the pan and cook for 1 minute. Drain under cold running water to cool quickly. Put the chicken, spinach and blanched vegetables in a serving bowl.

2 To make the sweet and sour dressing, combine the dressing ingredients in a screw-top jar, season with pepper and shake well to mix. Pour over the salad and toss to coat in the dressing.

3 To make the minted bulgur wheat, put the bulgur wheat in a bowl and pour over the boiling water. Stir well, then cover and steam for 15 minutes, or until the water has absorbed. Fluff up the grains with a fork, then mix in the chopped mint. Serve with the chicken salad.

COOK'S TIP
If you prefer, buy a cooked chicken (without stuffing) to save time. Alternatively, gently poach a whole chicken breast in a covered saucepan in chicken stock (add a few leaves of fresh mint for extra flavor) for about 10 minutes, or until the chicken is tender and cooked through. Remove from the saucepan, wrap in foil and set aside until cool enough to slice or shred.

GI LOW
Per serving (¹/₂ cup chicken, ¹/₂ cup cooked bulgur,
2 cups vegetables, 1 Tbsp dressing)
310 Cal, 8 g fat (saturated .5 g),
34 g protein, 28 g carbohydrate, 7 g fiber, 4 g sugar,
600 mg sodium

Equals: 1 Nutrisystem® Lunch + 1 Protein

ROAST PUMPKIN AND CHICKPEA SALAD SERVES 6

This sun-dried tomato dressing is not only delicious with pumpkin and chickpeas but can also be tossed through pasta, potatoes or steamed vegetables. Soaking time: Overnight Preparation time: 15 minutes Cooking time: 1½ hours

1 cup chickpeas, soaked overnight in water
5 cups (1 lb 10 oz) pumpkin, cut into
large cubes
olive oil spray
2 tablespoons chopped cilantro
or mint leaves

SUN-DRIED TOMATO DRESSING
1½ tablespoons red wine vinegar
¼ cup sun-dried tomatoes
2 tablespoons extra-virgin olive oil
1 garlic clove
2 teaspoons balsamic vinegar
2 teaspoons sugar
2 teaspoons lemon juice
freshly ground black pepper

1 Drain the chickpeas from the soaking water and rinse. Put the chickpeas in a large saucepan and cover with fresh water. Bring to a boil and cook for 40–50 minutes, or until tender. Drain and allow to cool.

2 Preheat the oven to 400°F. Put the pumpkin on a baking tray lined with parchment paper. Spray the pumpkin with olive oil and roast for 30–40 minutes, or until the pumpkin is tender and lightly caramelized. Allow to cool.

3 To make the sun-dried tomato dressing, put the red wine vinegar and tomatoes in a saucepan over low heat. Allow the tomatoes to soak in the hot vinegar to soften. Transfer the softened tomatoes to the bowl of a food processor and add the remaining dressing ingredients. Process to combine (don't overprocess—the texture should remain a little chunky).

4 Toss the pumpkin and chickpeas in the dressing, place in individual serving bowls or on a platter and sprinkle with the cilantro or mint.

COOK'S TIPS

If you don't have a food processor, roughly chop the softened tomatoes by hand, as we have done here, then combine with the remaining dressing ingredients.

Dried chickpeas are used here, and need to be soaked overnight before cooking. To save time, substitute with canned chickpeas.

G GI LOW
Per serving (²/₃ cup)
200 Cal, 7 g fat (saturated 1 g),
8 g protein, 29 g carbohydrate, 7 g fiber, 7 g sugar,
55 mg sodium

Equals: 1 Nutrisystem® Lunch

Recipe: Julie Le Clerc

BARLEY AND VEGETABLE SOUP SERVES 4

Preparation time: 15 minutes Cooking time: 40 minutes

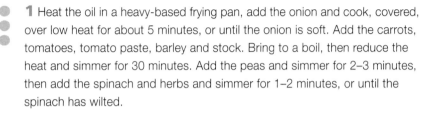

1 teaspoon olive oil
1 onion, chopped
2 small carrots, chopped
1 – 14 oz can tomatoes
1 tablespoon tomato paste
½ cup pearl barley
4 cups reduced sodium vegetable stock
⅔ cup fresh or frozen peas
4 cups baby spinach leaves, shredded
¼ cup mixed herbs, such as parsley, basil and oregano, roughly chopped
freshly ground black pepper

1 Heat the oil in a heavy-based frying pan, add the onion and cook, covered, over low heat for about 5 minutes, or until the onion is soft. Add the carrots, tomatoes, tomato paste, barley and stock. Bring to a boil, then reduce the heat and simmer for 30 minutes. Add the peas and simmer for 2–3 minutes, then add the spinach and herbs and simmer for 1–2 minutes, or until the spinach has wilted.

2 Divide the hot soup between four bowls. Season with pepper and serve with low GI bread of your choice, if desired.

GI LOW

Per serving (2 cups)
190 Cal, 1.5 g fat (saturated 0 g),
6 g protein, 38 g carbohydrate, 9 g fiber, 8 g sugar,
440 mg sodium

Equals: 1 Nutrisystem® Lunch

Recipe: Penny Hunking, Energise Nutrition

LENTIL, SPINACH AND FETA SALAD SERVES 4

The slightly peppery tasting French lentils are ideal for salads because they hold their shape when cooked, although they tend to take a little longer to cook than other lentils. Use brown lentils as a substitute if French are not available, but watch the cooking times as they can turn mushy if you overcook them. Preparation time: 10 minutes Cooking time: 35 minutes

1 cup French lentils
2 garlic cloves, flattened with
the side of a knife
2 red peppers
5½ cups baby spinach leaves
3 oz reduced fat feta cheese, cubed
1 tablespoon good-quality olive oil
2 teaspoons balsamic vinegar
1 teaspoon sugar, optional

1 Put the lentils in a saucepan, cover with water, add the flattened garlic cloves and bring to a boil. Reduce the heat and simmer for 25 minutes, or until the lentils are soft (these lentils should retain their shape). Remove the garlic and drain.

2 Quarter the peppers and remove the seeds. Place the peppers, skin-side up, under a broiler and cook until the skins are completely black. Allow to cool for 6–8 minutes, then remove the skins. Slice the flesh into strips.

3 Combine the lentils, pepper, spinach and feta cheese in a serving bowl. Pour over the oil and balsamic vinegar, sprinkle with sugar and mix well. Serve at room temperature.

ACTIVITY TIP
Arrange social get-togethers that involve some activity rather than centered solely on eating and drinking—meet for a walk, go bowling or have a picnic in the park.

 GI LOW

Per serving (2 cups with ¼ Tbsp olive oil)
290 Cal, 8 g fat (saturated 2.5 g),
19 g protein, 38 g carbohydrate, 11 g fiber, 5 g sugar,
360 mg sodium

Equals: 1 Nutrisystem® Lunch + 2 Vegetable

GOLDEN CARROT SOUP SERVES 4

Soups are wonderfully filling, full of nutrients and if you make them right provide all this with few calories—great for any weight loss program. Use winter carrots for this soup, as they have more flavor than the tiny spring and summer carrots.

Preparation time: 10 minutes Cooking time: 25 minutes

2 tablespoons olive oil
5 large winter carrots (about 2 lb 4 oz), chopped
1 large onion, chopped
2 garlic cloves, minced
3 bay leaves
5 cups reduced sodium beef or chicken stock
freshly ground black pepper
flat-leaf parsley, to serve

1 Heat the oil in a large saucepan. Add the carrots, onion, garlic and bay leaves and cook for 10 minutes.

2 Put the stock in another saucepan and bring to a boil. Pour the boiling stock over the vegetables and simmer for 15 minutes, or until tender. Remove the pan from the heat and remove the bay leaves. Allow the soup to cool a little, then transfer to a food processor or blender and purée until smooth. Season with pepper. If the soup is too thick, add some extra stock. Serve garnished with parsley.

COOK'S TIP
As a variation, garnish the soup with small bits of crispy bacon, or top with a dollop of garlic-flavored low-fat yogurt.

GI LOW
Per serving (1¹/₂ cups)
140 Cal, 7 g fat (saturated 1 g),
4 g protein, 15 g carbohydrate, 3 g fiber, 8 g sugar,
140 mg sodium

Equals: 1 Nutrisystem® Lunch

Recipe: Steffan Rössner

SMOKED SALMON AND DILL WITH PASTA SALAD   SERVES 6

This special-occasion salad makes a light meal for four or an exquisite starter for six. If serving as a main meal, accompany with a cucumber salad tossed with an oil and vinegar dressing.   Preparation time: 15 minutes   Cooking time: 10 minutes

9 oz penne pasta
5¼ oz smoked salmon, cut into strips
6 cherry tomatoes, halved,
or quartered if large
6 scallions, thinly sliced on the diagonal
1 small red onion, cut into thin rings,
slices separated
1 cup low-fat natural yogurt (optional)

DRESSING
⅓ cup extra-virgin olive oil
3 scallions, finely sliced
juice of ½ lemon
½ cup chopped dill
freshly ground black pepper

1 To make the dressing, combine the oil, scallions, lemon juice and dill in a food processor and purée until smooth. Season with pepper.

2 Cook the pasta in plenty of boiling water until al dente. Drain and rinse under cold running water until cool. Drain well and place in the serving dish. Pour over the dressing, then add the smoked salmon, tomatoes, scallions and onion rings. Toss gently to coat the pasta in the dressing. Serve with a dollop of yogurt, if using.

COOK'S TIPS
Penne is a finely ridged pasta. Ridged or ribbed pastas tend to hold on to more sauce than smooth pastas.

Avoid overcooking your pasta—not only does al dente pasta taste better, but it has a lower GI than pasta that has been cooked for too long.

G GI LOW
Per serving (1 cup)
340 Cal, 15 g fat (saturated 2.5 g),
13 g protein, 40 g carbohydrate, 3 g fiber, 7 g sugar,
230 mg sodium

Equals: 1 Nutrisystem® Lunch + 1 Protein + 1 Vegetable

Recipe: Loukie Werle, Trattoria Pasta

BARBECUED CHILE MINT LAMB AND TOMATO SALAD SERVES 2

This tasty salad uses the classic flavor combination of lamb, mint and tomatoes. Serve the zesty bulgur on the side, or toss it through the salad at the end, as we've done here. Preparation time: 20 minutes Cooking time: 25 minutes

6 oz lamb fillet, trimmed
extra-virgin olive oil, for brushing
1 cup mint leaves, roughly torn
4 small vine-ripened tomatoes, cut into
eighths, or 8 cherry tomatoes, halved
1/2 red pepper, sliced into strips
1 small cucumber, sliced into rounds
1 red chile, seeds removed and
thinly sliced (optional)
freshly ground black pepper
2 teaspoons extra-virgin olive oil
juice of 1/2 lemon

ZESTY BULGUR WHEAT
1/2 cup bulgur wheat
1/2 cup boiling water
finely grated zest and juice of 1 lemon

1 Lightly brush the lamb fillet with a little oil. Cook on a grill or in a frying pan for 3–4 minutes on each side, or until cooked to your liking. Remove the meat, wrap in foil and leave it to rest for 10 minutes.

2 Put the mint, tomatoes, pepper, cucumber and chile, if using, in a serving bowl. Season with pepper. Make a dressing by combining the oil and lemon juice in a screw-top jar and shake well.

3 To make the zesty bulgur wheat, put the bulgur wheat in a bowl and pour over the boiling water. Cover with foil (or plastic wrap or a plate) and leave to steam for about 15 minutes, or until the water has absorbed. Fluff up the grains with a fork and mix in the lemon zest and juice.

4 Slice the lamb fillet thinly across the grain, toss with the salad ingredients and the bulgur wheat, then pour over the dressing and toss to coat.

ACTIVITY TIP
A recent study found that those who walked regularly with a dog lost more weight than those who walked alone. If you don't have your own dog, offer to walk a neighbor's—you will both end up reaping the rewards.

GI LOW Ⓖ

Per serving (approximately 1³/₄ cups)
330 Cal, 10 g fat (saturated 2.5 g),
25 g protein, 40 g carbohydrate, 10 g fiber, 8 g sugar,
65 mg sodium

Equals: 1 Nutrisystem® Lunch + 1 Protein + 1 Vegetable

COUSCOUS SALAD SERVES 4–6

Although couscous has a medium GI, combining it with chickpeas, as we have done here, means that the overall meal has a low GI. This couscous salad is delicious as a meal in itself or served as an accompaniment for chicken or meat dishes.

Preparation time: 15 minutes

1 cup couscous
1 cup canned chickpeas,
rinsed and drained
½ small bunch flat-leaf
parsley, chopped
½ small bunch cilantro
leaves, chopped
1 tablespoon ground cumin
½ red pepper, chopped
½ green pepper, chopped
1 cup chopped mixed dried fruit, such as
apricots, dates, currants, figs
2 tablespoons pistachio nuts
2 tablespoons pine nuts, toasted

DRESSING
2 tablespoons extra-virgin olive oil
juice of 1 lemon
freshly ground black pepper

1 Make the couscous according to the package directions—you should end up with about 2 cups cooked couscous. Make sure the couscous is quite dry before using it.

2 Put the couscous in a large serving bowl and combine with the chickpeas, parsley, cilantro, cumin, peppers, dried fruit, pistachios and pine nuts.

3 To make the dressing, put the oil and lemon juice in a screw-top jar. Season with pepper, shake well, then pour over the couscous salad and toss to coat.

G GI LOW

Per serving (1 cup salad)
290 Cal, 8 g fat (saturated 1 g),
7 g protein, 50 g carbohydrate, 7 g fiber, 11 g sugar,
150 mg sodium

Equals: 1 Nutrisystem® Lunch + 1 Protein

CHICKEN, MINT AND CORN SOUP SERVES 4

For the sweetest flavor, buy corn on the cob with the husk intact, because the natural sugar in the kernels starts converting into starch the moment the green husk is removed. Fresh cooked corn has a low GI of 48. Frozen kernels are a suitable substitute for fresh in this recipe. Preparation time: 10 minutes Cooking time: 20 minutes

2 corn cobs
4 cups reduced sodium chicken stock
6 mint leaves, plus extra to garnish
4 – 6 oz skinless chicken breast fillets
²/₃ cup snow pea sprouts
2 teaspoons julienned lemon rind
freshly ground black pepper

1 Put the corn cobs in a large saucepan of boiling water and cook for 10 minutes. Remove the cobs and cut off the kernels. Set aside.

2 Put the chicken stock and mint leaves in a poaching pan or large saucepan and bring to a boil. Add the chicken, return to a simmer and poach for 10–12 minutes, or until the chicken is cooked through. Just before the chicken is ready, add the corn kernels and snow pea sprouts to the hot stock.

3 Remove the chicken, slice on the diagonal, then divide between four bowls. Ladle the broth and vegetables into the bowls. Garnish with the lemon rind and extra mint. Season with pepper.

GI LOW Ⓖ

Per serving (1¹/₂ cups)
140 Cal, 2 g fat (saturated .5 g),
14 g protein, 14 g carbohydrate, 4 g fiber, 5 g sugar,
250 mg sodium

Equals: 1 Nutrisystem® Lunch

Recipe: Luke Mangan

LUKE MANGAN

CURRIED LENTIL SALAD SERVES 4

One of our key guidelines in The Low GI Diet Revolution *is to eat more legumes such as beans, chickpeas and lentils—in fact, we recommend you have a meal that includes legumes at least twice a week. This curried lentil salad will make that easy!*
Preparation time: 10 minutes Cooking time: 20–25 minutes

1 tablespoon poly- or monounsaturated margarine
1 tablespoon curry powder
1½ cups French or brown lentils
1 small red onion, thinly sliced
8 cherry tomatoes, halved
2 cups baby spinach leaves
¼ cup cilantro leaves
¼ cup mint leaves
2 tablespoons red wine vinegar
2 tablespoons extra-virgin olive oil
sea salt and freshly ground black pepper

1 Melt the margarine in a saucepan and add the curry powder. Stir for about 20 seconds, then add the lentils, stirring to coat well. Add a generous pinch of salt. Cover the lentils with water, bring to a simmer and cook for 20 minutes, or until the lentils are soft. (Take care not to let the lentils get too dry—add more water if necessary, but don't make them too wet.) Remove from the heat, drain, rinse and set aside to cool.

2 Put the cooled lentils in a large bowl with the onion, tomatoes, spinach and herbs. Whisk together the vinegar and oil, pour over the salad and toss well. Season to taste with sea salt and pepper.

Ⓖ GI LOW

Per serving (1 cup salad)
350 Cal, 9 g fat (saturated 1.5 g),
20 g protein, 49 g carbohydrate,
    24 g fiber, 4 g sugar,
40 mg sodium

**Equals: 1 Nutrisystem® Lunch +
1 Vegetable + 1 Fat**

Luke Mangan is one of Australia's best-known and talented chefs. He has opened three restaurants in Sydney: Salt (which won two chef's hats), Bistro Lulu, and Moorish. In 2004 he was invited to cook for the wedding festivities of Crown Prince Frederik and Mary Donaldson in Denmark and he has also cooked for other guests such as Bill Clinton and Sir Richard Branson. Sir Richard Branson consequently appointed him food consultant for Virgin Atlantic Airways on the Sydney-to-London route launched in December 2004. Luke is also author of three cookbooks—*Breakfast, Lunch, Dinner (BLD); Luke Mangan Food;* and *Luke Mangan Classics.* He travels widely, promoting Australian food and wine.

SOBA NOODLE SOUP WITH SHRIMP AND TOFU SERVES 4

Tofu, whether you buy the soft or firm variety, absorbs other flavors well and makes a delicious addition to stir-fries and soups such as this one. Preparation time: 20 minutes Cooking time: 10 minutes

3½ oz soba noodles
4 cups reduced sodium vegetable stock
2 teaspoons grated ginger
2 tablespoons reduced sodium soy sauce
1 tablespoon mirin
2 teaspoons sugar
1–2 small red chiles, seeded and finely chopped
24 large shrimp, raw, peeled and deveined, with tails intact
2 scallions, sliced on the diagonal
2 cups baby spinach leaves, shredded
10½ oz silken firm tofu, cut into ¾ in cubes
¼ cup cilantro leaves

1 Cook the soba noodles in a saucepan of boiling water for 4 minutes, or until tender. Drain and set aside.

2 Combine the stock, ginger, soy sauce, mirin, sugar and chiles in a large saucepan. Bring to a boil, then reduce the heat and simmer for 3 minutes. Add the shrimp, scallions and spinach and simmer for 2 minutes, or until the shrimp turn pink and are cooked.

3 Divide the noodles and tofu evenly between four bowls. Spoon over the broth and serve garnished with cilantro.

GI LOW

Per serving (approximately 1 cup broth with noodles, 6 shrimp, 4 cubes of tofu)
230 Cal, 2.5 g fat (saturated 0 g),
19 g protein, 31 g carbohydrate, 2 g fiber, 6 g sugar,
600 mg sodium

Equals: 1 Nutrisystem® Lunch + 1 Protein

FRAGRANT BULGUR WHEAT WITH ZEST SERVES 4

Bulgur wheat is used extensively in Middle Eastern cooking and not only has a low GI (48) but is delicious and takes only minutes to prepare. Try this salad as an accompaniment to chicken, or pan-fried marinated tofu slices for a vegetarian meal.

Preparation time: 15 minutes Cooking time: 17 minutes

1 cup bulgur wheat
1 cup boiling water
1 tablespoon olive oil
1 tablespoon finely chopped lemon grass
1 tablespoon grated ginger
grated zest of ½ lemon
grated zest of ½ lime
1 tablespoon lemon juice
1 tablespoon lime juice
2 vine-ripened tomatoes, chopped
4 scallions, thinly sliced on the diagonal
12 asparagus spears, blanched, cut on the diagonal into 1 in pieces
freshly ground black pepper
2 tablespoons chopped parsley

LEMON YOGURT
1 cup low-fat natural yogurt
1 tablespoon lemon juice
2 tablespoons chopped chives

1 Put the bulgur wheat in a bowl and pour over 1 cup boiling water. Stir well, then cover with foil (or plastic wrap or a plate) and steam for about 15 minutes, or until all of the water has absorbed.

2 Heat the oil in a non-stick frying pan over medium heat, add the lemon grass and ginger and fry for 2 minutes. Add the lemon and lime zest and juice. Add the bulgur wheat and mix well. Transfer to a serving bowl and add the tomatoes, scallions and asparagus and toss to combine. Season with pepper and sprinkle with parsley.

3 To make the lemon yogurt, put all the ingredients in a bowl and mix to combine, adding a little more lemon juice if it is too thick. To serve, drizzle the yogurt over the bulgur wheat salad.

Ⓖ GI LOW

Per serving (1 cup)
220 Cal, 4.5 g fat (saturated .5 g),
8 g protein, 41 g carbohydrate, 9 g fiber, 9 g sugar,
45 mg sodium

Equals: 1 Nutrisystem® Lunch + 1 Vegetable

Recipe: Jill McMillan

BLACK BEAN SOUP SERVES 6

This tangy, nourishing soup shows you how easy it is to incorporate legumes into your weekly meal plans. Black beans, also called turtle beans, have a mild, earthy taste when cooked. They are widely used throughout Latin America and the Caribbean.

Soaking time: Overnight Preparation time: 15 minutes Cooking time: 1 hour

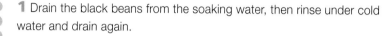

1 cup dried black beans,
soaked overnight in water
1 tablespoon olive oil
2 onions, roughly chopped
2 garlic cloves, minced
3 slices bacon, fat trimmed, chopped
2 teaspoons ground cumin
1 teaspoon ground coriander
2 carrots, chopped
1 lb orange sweet potato, cubed
2 bay leaves
6 cups chicken or vegetable stock
¼ cup chopped cilantro leaves
freshly ground black pepper

1 Drain the black beans from the soaking water, then rinse under cold water and drain again.

2 Heat the oil in a large saucepan. Add the onions, garlic and bacon and cook for 4 minutes, or until the onion is soft. Add the cumin and ground coriander and cook for about 30 seconds, or until aromatic. Add the carrots, sweet potato, bay leaves, stock and beans. Bring to a boil, then cover and simmer over low heat for 1 hour, or until the beans and vegetables are soft.

3 Remove the bay leaves from the soup. Allow to cool a little, then transfer to a food processor or blender and purée until smooth. Mix in the cilantro and season with pepper.

COOK'S TIPS

Although they will keep indefinitely, it's best to use legumes within 1 year of purchase. Before cooking, be sure to pick through them, picking out any small pebbles, split and withered beans and any other foreign matter.

Don't add salt to the cooking water—it slows down water absorption and cooking takes longer.

You can keep soaked or cooked beans in an airtight container for several days in the refrigerator.

GI LOW

Per serving (1³/₄ cups)
240 Cal, 4 g fat (saturated 1 g),
10 g protein, 43 g carbohydrate, 11 g fiber, 15 g sugar,
570 mg sodium

Equals: 1 Nutrisystem® Lunch + 1 Protein

WHITE BEAN SALAD SERVES 4

Preparation time: 10 minutes Cooking time: 2 minutes

12 asparagus spears, trimmed
2 teaspoons pure floral honey
2 teaspoons olive oil
2 tablespoons red wine vinegar
16 cherry tomatoes, halved
1 – 14 oz can white beans, rinsed and drained
2 tablespoons chopped parsley
freshly ground black pepper

1 Bring a large frying pan filled with water to a gentle simmer. Place the asparagus in the water and cook for 1–2 minutes, or until tender. Refresh under cold water, then chop into 1¼ in lengths.

2 To make a dressing for the bean salad, put the honey, oil and vinegar in a small screw-top jar and shake to combine.

3 Put the tomatoes, beans, parsley and cooled asparagus in a bowl. Pour over the dressing, toss to combine, then season with pepper.

G GI LOW

Per serving (1 cup)
120 Cal, 2.5 g fat (saturated 0 g),
6 g protein, 19 g carbohydrate, 5 g fiber, 7 g sugar,
190 mg sodium

Equals: 1 Nutrisystem® Lunch

SWEET CHILE TUNA SALAD SERVES 2

Preparation time: 10 minutes

4 iceberg lettuce leaves, shredded
¼ red pepper finely chopped
1 tomato, chopped
½ red onion, finely chopped
2 – 3¼ oz cans sweet chile tuna
1 cup crispy soy noodles
juice of 1 lime
cilantro leaves, to garnish

1 Combine the lettuce, pepper, tomato and onion in a serving bowl. Add the tuna and noodles. Squeeze the lime juice over, add the cilantro leaves and toss to combine. Serve immediately.

COOK'S TIP

If you can't find canned sweet chile tuna, use canned tuna in springwater and add 1 tablespoon sweet chile sauce to each can.

G GI LOW

Per serving (½ cup noodles and 1 can tuna)
300 Cal, 9 g fat (saturated 2 g),
27 g protein, 27 g carbohydrate, 3 g fiber, 5 g sugar,
580 mg sodium

Equals: 1 Nutrisystem® Lunch + 1 Protein + 1 Vegetable

Right: Sweet chile tuna salad

VIETNAMESE BEEF SOUP SERVES 6

Pho bo, a beef soup with rice noodles, is often referred to as Vietnam's national dish and is eaten at any time of day. A boiling broth is poured over the thinly sliced raw beef and is hot enough to cook the beef. Separate aromatic seasonings such as chile and Vietnamese mint are often served on the side. Preparation time: 20 minutes Cooking time: 35 minutes

STOCK
2 teaspoons olive oil
1 garlic clove, minced
1 small onion, chopped
1½ in piece ginger, thinly sliced
6 cups reduced sodium beef stock
1 cinnamon stick
1 star anise
1 lemon grass stick, lightly bruised
1 tablespoon fish sauce
1 tablespoon reduced sodium soy sauce
1 teaspoon sugar

1 lb 2 oz fresh rice noodles
7 oz beef eye fillet, very thinly sliced
1 cup bean sprouts
2 tablespoons roughly chopped cilantro leaves
4 scallions, thinly sliced
1–2 small red chiles, to taste, seeded and very thinly sliced
½ lime, cut into wedges

1 To make the soup, begin with the stock. Heat the oil in a large saucepan and add the garlic, onion and ginger and stir-fry until aromatic. Add 4 cups water, beef stock, cinnamon, star anise, lemon grass, fish sauce, soy sauce and sugar. Bring to a boil, then reduce the heat and simmer, uncovered, for 30 minutes. Cool about 10 minutes. Strain the stock, return the liquid to the pan and return to a boil.

2 Put the fresh rice noodles in a bowl, cover with boiling water and leave to soak for a few minutes. When the noodles have softened a little, gently separate them, then drain. Divide the noodles between four deep bowls, top with the beef slices, bean sprouts and cilantro, then pour over the boiling stock. Garnish with scallions and chiles and serve with the lime wedges for squeezing over.

ACTIVITY TIP

For all short trips that would take less than 5 minutes in the car, take the time to walk instead. Go shopping on foot and carry your bags home—a fantastic total body workout! However, if you have to drive to the nearest shopping center, park the car in the furthest parking spot and walk the rest of the way.

GI LOW
Per serving (2 cups)
260 Cal, 11 g fat (saturated 3.5 g),
12 g protein, 28 g carbohydrate, 2 g fiber, 4 g sugar,
410 mg sodium

Equals: 1 Nutrisystem® Lunch + 1 Protein

Recipe: Lynne Mullins, Noodles to Pasta

DINNER

WHAT'S FOR DINNER? HERE'S HOW WE DO IT.
WE CHOOSE THE CARBOHYDRATE: SWEET
POTATO, RICE, PASTA, NOODLES, GRAINS,
LEGUMES OR A COMBINATION. THEN WE ADD
VEGETABLES—LOTS OF THEM—EITHER FRESH,
FROZEN OR CANNED. FINALLY, WE INCLUDE
PROTEIN FOR NUTRIENTS, FLAVOR, AND SATIETY
FACTOR, BUT WE MAKE SURE IT'S LOW
IN SATURATED FAT.

TUNA POACHED IN TOMATO AND FENNEL WITH CHILE CHICKPEA MASH SERVES 4

Mashed legumes make a great low GI and nutrient-rich alternative to mashed potatoes. The mash also makes a delicious spread on its own, rather like hummus—if you like it hot, add extra chile. Preparation time: 20 minutes Cooking time: 45 minutes

1 tablespoon extra-virgin olive oil
2 large fennel bulbs or 4 baby fennel bulbs, thickly sliced (tops reserved)
1 large red onion, sliced
2 garlic cloves, minced
1 – 15½ oz can peeled Italian tomatoes, chopped
1 cup dry white wine
2 in long strip of lemon zest
1 bay leaf
1 lb 2 oz tuna steaks, cut into large bite-sized chunks
freshly ground black pepper
2 tablespoons chopped flat-leaf parsley
1 tablespoon chopped fennel tops
lemon wedges, to serve

CHILE CHICKPEA MASH
1 – 15½ oz can chickpeas, rinsed and drained
1 small red chile, seeded and thinly sliced
2 tablespoons chopped flat-leaf parsley
juice of ½ lemon
½ cup boiling water
freshly ground black pepper

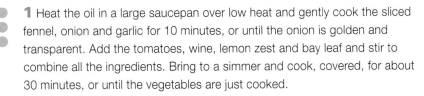

1 Heat the oil in a large saucepan over low heat and gently cook the sliced fennel, onion and garlic for 10 minutes, or until the onion is golden and transparent. Add the tomatoes, wine, lemon zest and bay leaf and stir to combine all the ingredients. Bring to a simmer and cook, covered, for about 30 minutes, or until the vegetables are just cooked.

2 Place the tuna chunks in the vegetable mixture, gently stir, then poach for 3–4 minutes.

3 While the tuna is poaching, make the chile chickpea mash. Put the chickpeas in a food processor with the chile, parsley and lemon juice and purée, adding just enough of the boiling water to make a smooth, creamy mixture. Season with pepper.

4 Remove the strip of lemon zest and bay leaf from the tuna and season with pepper. Place a scoop of warm chile chickpea mash onto each plate and top with the tuna and vegetable mixture. Scatter over the chopped parsley and fennel tops. Serve with lemon wedges, and with crunchy grainy bread for mopping up the juices, if desired.

COOK'S TIP
Fennel is delicious thinly sliced and served raw in salads or cooked. Choose bulbs with green, sweet-smelling leaves. Remove the tough outer stalks as they are usually damaged or stringy, trim the base of the bulb, then halve, quarter, slice or dice. Chop the feathery tops and use as a garnish, or add to sauces or dressings at the end of cooking time.

G GI LOW

Per serving (3 oz tuna, ½ cup tomato mixture, ⅓ cup chickpea mash)
440 Cal, 11 g fat (saturated 2 g),
39 g protein, 43 g carbohydrate, 10 g fiber, 6 g sugar,
670 mg sodium

Equals: 1 Nutrisystem® Dinner + 1 Protein + 1 Fruit/Vegetable + 1 Fat

VEAL TAGINE WITH SWEET POTATOES SERVES 4

The word tagine refers both to the Moroccan cooking pot—traditionally a round clay pot with a conical lid—as well as the stew you cook in it. If you don't have a tagine, a Dutch oven will do just as well. For the best results, make your own tagine spice mix; otherwise, buy a prepared mix. Preparation time: 20 minutes Cooking time: 1¼ hours

1 lb 2 oz veal, trimmed and cut into 1 in cubes
2 tablespoons extra-virgin olive oil
2 red onions, sliced
2 garlic cloves, minced
4 tomatoes (about 10½ oz), quartered
2 orange sweet potatoes (about 1 lb 2 oz), thickly sliced
1 red pepper, halved and sliced
¼ cup chopped cilantro leaves (optional)

TAGINE SPICE MIX
5 teaspoons mild paprika
2 teaspoons ground coriander
1 teaspoon ground cinnamon
1 teaspoon cayenne pepper
½ teaspoon allspice
¼ teaspoon ground cloves
¼ teaspoon ground green cardamom

1 To make the tagine spice mix, combine all the spices in a large bowl.

2 To make the tagine, toss the veal in the spice mix to coat. Heat the oil in a 4-quart Dutch oven over high heat and quickly brown the meat pieces on all sides. Remove with a slotted spoon and set aside. Reduce the heat to medium, add the onions and garlic and cook gently for 5 minutes, or until the onions are golden and translucent.

3 Return the veal to the dish and add the tomatoes, sweet potatoes, pepper and 1 cup water. Stir gently to combine, then cover with a piece of parchment paper (this helps reduce evaporation) and the lid and simmer gently for 1 hour, or until the meat is tender. Garnish with cilantro, if using.

4 This tagine is a meal in itself, or you can serve with steamed basmati rice or bulgur wheat, if desired.

COOK'S TIP
The pods of green cardamom are bright green and not to be confused with brown cardamom, as they are not interchangeable in recipes. Green cardamom has a sweet eucalyptus-like aroma that adds a light, fresh taste to spice mixes. Brown has a distinct "musty-smoky" flavor. You can buy green cardamom in larger supermarkets and specialist spice stores.

GI LOW Ⓖ

Per serving (4 oz veal, ¾ cup vegetable mixture)
380 Cal, 12 g fat (saturated 2 g),
30 g protein, 39 g carbohydrate, 7 g fiber 11 g sugar,
190 mg sodium

Equals: 1 Nutrisystem® Dinner + 1 Fruit/Vegetable + 1 Fat

Tagine spice mix: Liz and Ian Hemphill, Herbies Spices

LINGUINE WITH SALMON AND PEAS SERVES 6

If you are a fan of the "meal in a bowl", then this recipe is just right for you. It's also packed with sustaining low GI carbs, vegetables and protein for that perfect satiety factor. Best of all, it's on the table in around 30 minutes.

Preparation time: 15 minutes Cooking time: 17 minutes

12 oz linguine
12 oz salmon fillets, skinned
1 tablespoon extra-virgin olive oil
2 cups fresh or frozen peas
1 cup fish or vegetable stock
2 tablespoons chopped flat-leaf parsley
freshly ground black pepper
juice of 1 lemon, or to taste
1 teaspoon finely grated lemon zest,
or to taste

1 Bring a large saucepan of water to a boil and cook the pasta until al dente.

2 Meanwhile, carefully check the salmon for any bones, then cut into bite-sized pieces. Heat the oil in a large deep frying pan until the oil is shimmering, then add the salmon pieces and cook gently for about 5 minutes, or until the salmon changes color and is cooked through, being careful not to brown it. Add the peas, stock and parsley and cook for 1–2 minutes. Season with plenty of pepper, then add the lemon juice and zest, to taste, stirring gently to combine all the ingredients.

3 When the pasta is cooked, drain well and add to the sauce, tossing lightly to coat the pasta in the sauce. Serve immediately.

 GI LOW

Per serving (¹⁄₄ cup linguine, 2 oz fish)
310 Cal, 3 g fat (saturated .5 g),
21 g protein, 50 g carbohydrate, 4 g fiber, 3 g sugar,
120 mg sodium

Equals: 1 Nutrisystem® Dinner + 1 Fat

BEEF STROGANOFF SERVES 6

Beef stroganoff is usually loaded with sour cream, which pushes up the saturated fat content. This version uses natural yogurt instead of sour cream. The GI of this recipe is medium, which is due to the basmati rice—to lower the GI, you may prefer to use half rice and half barley. Preparation time: 15 minutes Cooking time: 20 minutes

1½ cups basmati rice
1 lb 2 oz lean beef, cut into strips
1 tablespoon olive oil
1 red onion, thinly sliced
1 onion, thinly sliced
2 large garlic cloves, minced
9 oz mushrooms, sliced
¼ cup brandy (optional)
zest and juice of 1 orange
½ teaspoon dried dill or 1 tablespoon chopped dill
freshly ground black pepper
1 cup low-fat natural yogurt

1 Wash the rice and put it in a large saucepan with 2 cups water. Cover with the lid and bring to a boil, then reduce the heat and simmer for 10 minutes. Turn off the heat and leave to stand, without removing the lid, until ready to serve.

2 Meanwhile, heat a large non-stick frying pan over medium heat. Dry-fry the meat, in small batches, for 2 minutes. Remove the meat and set aside.

3 Using the same pan, heat the oil over medium heat, add the onions and garlic and fry for 5 minutes, or until the onions are soft. Add the mushrooms and fry for 3 minutes. Return the meat to the pan.

4 If using brandy, pour it into the pan and flambé, then dowse the flames with the orange zest and orange juice. Add the dill and season with lots of pepper. Turn off the heat before mixing in the yogurt.

5 Spoon the steamed rice onto plates and top with the stroganoff. You may like to serve this with a mixed green salad or steamed vegetables.

ACTIVITY TIP

Try out a new activity. For example, join a dance class: salsa, ballroom, line dancing or jazz; go rollerblading with friends; book in for golf or tennis lessons; or take your children to the park. You can't afford not to exercise, so find something you enjoy and get moving!

GI MEDIUM

Per serving (½ cup rice, ½ cup beef mixture)
360 Cal, 9 g fat (saturated 3 g),
24 g protein, 44 g carbohydrate, 2 g fiber 4 g sugar,
80 mg sodium

Equals: 1 Nutrisystem® Dinner + 1 Fruit/Vegetable + 1 Fat

Recipe: Isobel McMillan

SPINACH AND RICOTTA CANNELLONI SERVES 4

This delicious dinner dish is easy to assemble using today's wonderful convenience foods. Buy a really good-quality, ready-to-serve tomato sauce or make your own favorite tomato sauce if you have the time.

Preparation time: 15 minutes Cooking time: 30 minutes

1 – 10½ oz package frozen spinach, defrosted
1 container (15 oz) fat-free ricotta cheese
¼ teaspoon ground nutmeg
2 tablespoons pine nuts, toasted
⅓ cup reduced sodium Parmesan cheese, finely grated
4 fresh lasagna sheets
10½ oz ready-to-serve tomato pasta sauce
freshly ground black pepper
torn basil leaves, to serve

1 Preheat the oven to 350°F. Put the spinach in a colander and squeeze out the excess liquid.

2 Combine the ricotta, nutmeg, pine nuts and half the Parmesan in a large bowl and mix with a wooden spoon. Lay one sheet of lasagna on a flat surface and spoon a quarter of the ricotta mixture along the long edge of the sheet. Roll lengthways to make a long sausage shape and place into an oblong lasagna dish, cutting the lasagna to fit if necessary. Repeat with the remaining ricotta mixture and lasagna sheets.

3 Spoon the pasta sauce over the cannelloni and season with pepper. Cover with foil and bake for 25–30 minutes, or until the pasta is tender and the sauce is bubbling.

4 Divide the lasagna into four and serve. Spoon any extra tomato sauce over the top, sprinkle with the remaining Parmesan and scatter over the basil.

ACTIVITY TIP
Become an active person by nature where you see every moment as an opportunity for movement, not an inconvenience. In other words, be the person who offers to run an errand, wash the car or walk to the local store. Every moment of activity counts in the long run.

G GI LOW

Per serving (1 cannelloni)
330 Cal, 10 g fat (saturated 2 g),
26 g protein, 35 g carbohydrate, 4 g fiber, 8 g sugar,
540 mg sodium

Equals: 1 Nutrisystem® Dinner + 1 Fruit/Vegetable + 1 Fat

ADUKI BEAN STEW SERVES 4

Aduki beans are eaten widely in their native Japan. They are one of the most delicious of all dried beans and have a sweet meaty flavor. The beans are soaked overnight to shorten the cooking time.

Soaking time: Overnight Preparation time: 15 minutes Cooking time: 45–50 minutes

1 cup dried aduki beans, soaked
overnight in water
1 leek, sliced
1 carrot, chopped
1 orange sweet potato (about 9 oz), cubed
1 chicken bouillon cube, crumbled
1 teaspoon Tabasco sauce
2 tablespoons tomato paste
1 tablespoon Worcestershire sauce
1 cup small broccoli florets
¼ cup chopped cilantro leaves
4 tablespoons low-fat natural yogurt
(optional)

1 Drain the beans from the soaking water and rinse well. Put the beans in a saucepan, cover with water and bring to a boil, then reduce the heat and simmer for 30–35 minutes, partially covered (the beans should still be a little hard after this time).

2 Add all other ingredients, except the broccoli and cilantro, and cook for 10 minutes. Add the broccoli and cilantro and simmer for 5 minutes, or until the broccoli is tender.

3 Serve in bowls topped with a spoonful of natural yogurt, if desired. You may like to serve this with steamed basmati rice or sourdough bread.

 COOK'S TIP
You may need to buy dried aduki beans from a health food store, as they are not as widely available as the canned version.

GI LOW
Per serving (1 cup)
260 Cal, .5 g fat (saturated 0 g),
13 g protein, 53 g carbohydrate, 10 g fiber, 6 g sugar,
540 mg sodium

Equals: 1 Nutrisystem® Dinner + 1 Protein

Recipe: Jill McMillan

CHICKEN AND BOK CHOY STIR-FRY SERVES 4

Preparation time: 10 minutes Cooking time: 10 minutes

8 oz dried egg noodles
2 teaspoons peanut oil
2 garlic cloves, minced
2 tablespoons grated ginger
2 skinless chicken breast fillets (about
6 oz each), cut into thin strips
leaves and stems from 3 heads bok choy,
roughly chopped
8 baby corn, halved
3 tablespoons reduced sodium soy sauce
1 tablespoon oyster sauce
1 red chile, seeded and thinly sliced
4 scallions, thinly sliced

1 Cook the noodles in plenty of boiling water for 4–5 minutes. Rinse in cold water, drain well and set aside.

2 Heat the oil in a wok and add the garlic and ginger. Stir-fry for a few seconds, or until aromatic, then add the chicken and stir-fry for 5 minutes, or until the chicken changes color. Add the bok choy and corn and stir until the bok choy is wilted, then add the soy sauce, oyster sauce and chile. Stir to coat the chicken in the sauce. Add the noodles and toss to heat through. Serve in bowls and sprinkle with scallions.

GI LOW Ⓖ

Per serving (1 cup)
370 Cal, 6 g fat (saturated 1.5 g),
30 g protein, 48 g carbohydrate, 3 g fiber, 3 g sugar,
490 mg sodium

Equals: 1 Nutrisystem® Dinner + 1 Fruit/Vegetable + 1 Fat

Recipe: Lynne Mullins, Noodles to Pasta

BEEF AND NOODLES WITH CHILE JAM SERVES 8

Preparation time: 10 minutes Cooking time: 15 minutes

2 tablespoons peanut oil
1 lb 2 oz beef rump steak,
thinly sliced
7 oz Thai chile jam
24 green beans, trimmed and cut
into 1¼ in pieces
12 baby corn, halved
½ cup chopped cilantro leaves
1 package (1 lb 2 oz) fresh Asian noodles,
such as Hokkien (egg) noodles

1 Heat 1 teaspoon of the oil in a wok or frying pan over medium heat. Stir-fry the beef, in batches, for about 3 minutes each batch, or until brown. Return all the beef to the wok, then add the chile jam, beans, corn and ¼ cup water. Stir-fry for 4 minutes, or until the vegetables are tender. Stir in the cilantro. Add the noodles to the wok and stir to combine. Heat through and serve.

GI LOW

Per serving (1 cup)
340 Cal, 16 g fat (saturated 3.5 g),
20 g protein, 31 g carbohydrate, 3 g fiber, 1 g sugar,
290 mg sodium

Equals: 1 Nutrisystem® Dinner + 1 Fruit/Vegetable + 1 Fat

Left: Beef and noodles with chile jam

PASTA WITH SCALLOPS AND WILD ARUGULA SERVES 6

Wild arugula has a stronger flavor than ordinary arugula and is perfect for salads with shaved Parmesan. Here the arugula's piquant, cresslike bite complements the richness of the scallops. Preparation time: 10 minutes Cooking time: 15 minutes

*12 oz dried pasta, such as spaghetti
or linguine
2 tablespoons extra-virgin olive oil
2 garlic cloves, minced
1 red chile, seeded and finely chopped
14 oz fresh scallops, cleaned and
prepared, halved if large
3 plum tomatoes, peeled and chopped
juice of 1 lemon
1 cup firmly packed wild arugula leaves
freshly ground black pepper*

1 Bring a large saucepan of water to a boil and cook the pasta until al dente.

2 Meanwhile, heat the oil in a large, deep frying pan or large saucepan over medium heat. Add the garlic and chile and cook, stirring, for 1–2 minutes, being careful that the garlic does not brown. Add the scallops and cook for 1–2 minutes on each side, or until just golden. Stir in the tomatoes and lemon juice and cook until heated through.

3 When the pasta is cooked, drain it thoroughly, then add to the sauce along with the arugula leaves. Season with pepper, then lightly toss the ingredients together. Serve immediately.

COOK'S TIP
To peel tomatoes, first remove the stems, then score a cross in the bottom of each tomato using a knife. Blanch the tomatoes in boiling water for 30–60 seconds. Transfer to a bowl of cold water, then peel the skin away from the cross.

Ⓖ GI LOW
Per serving (1 cup pasta, 3 scallops)
320 Cal, 6 g fat (saturated 1 g),
19 g protein, 47 g carbohydrate, 2 g fiber, 4 g sugar,
115 mg sodium

**Equals: 1 Nutrisystem® Dinner +
1 Fruit/Vegetable + 1 Fat**

GRILLED STEAK WITH CHILE CORN SALSA SERVES 2

This versatile corn salsa is delicious served with steaks, such as eye fillet or rump, and complements other meats too, including thinly sliced rare roast beef and barbecued chicken sausages. Preparation time: 10 minutes Cooking time: 12–15 minutes

2 – 3 oz small lean beef steaks
1 bunch arugula leaves

CHILE CORN SALSA
2 corn cobs
1 tomato, seeded and cut into small pieces
½ red onion, finely chopped
2 small red chiles, seeded, finely chopped
½ bunch chives, finely chopped
½ bunch cilantro, leaves picked and finely chopped
2 tablespoons balsamic vinegar
1 tablespoon extra-virgin olive oil

1 To make the chile corn salsa, put the corn cobs in a saucepan of boiling water and cook for 5 minutes. Drain. Use a sharp knife to cut the kernels from the cobs, then place them in a large bowl. Add the tomato, onion, chiles, half the chives and half the cilantro.

2 Whisk together the vinegar and oil and toss through the salsa.

3 Grill or panfry the steaks to your liking. To serve, put a steak on each plate, spoon a small mound of salsa on each steak and serve with the arugula. Garnish with the remaining herbs.

GI LOW Ⓖ

Per serving (1 steak with ½ cup salsa)
410 Cal, 21 g fat (saturated 6 g),
23 g protein, 35 g carbohydrate, 5 g fiber, 12 g sugar,
75 mg sodium

**Equals: 1 Nutrisystem® Dinner +
1 Fruit/Vegetable + 1 Fat**

Chile corn salsa recipe: Luke Mangan

PORK VINDALOO SERVES 5

Vindaloo curries are renowned for their heat, but if you like your vindaloo fiery, add an extra green chile or two. Serve with steamed basmati rice and your favorite curry accompaniments.

Marinating time: 1 hour Preparation time: 30 minutes Cooking time: 1½ hours

1 lb 10 oz pork cubes
2 tablespoons olive oil
2 onions, thinly sliced
4 garlic cloves, thinly sliced
1½ in piece ginger, cut into matchsticks
3 ripe tomatoes, chopped
2 green chiles, seeds removed, chopped
1 teaspoon soft brown sugar
½ cup chopped cilantro leaves

VINDALOO MARINADE
2 tablespoons vindaloo curry powder
(page 134, or prepared), or to taste
4 tablespoons white wine vinegar
1 tablespoon malt vinegar

2½ cups steamed basmati rice,
to serve
mung bean dhal (page 136),
to serve (optional)
cucumber raita (page 134),
to serve (optional)

1 To make the vindaloo marinade, combine the curry powder and vinegars together in a large non-metallic bowl and mix well.

2 Add the pork to the bowl and toss the pieces to coat in the marinade. Cover and leave to marinate in the refrigerator for 1 hour (or more if you have the time).

3 Heat the oil in a 4-quart Dutch oven over low heat and gently cook the onions until soft and golden. Add the garlic, ginger, tomatoes, chiles and sugar and stir well to combine. Add the pork (reserve the marinade), increase the heat and cook for 1–2 minutes, or until the meat is starting to brown. Add 1 cup water and the reserved marinade, cover and simmer for about 1–1½ hours, stirring occasionally, or until the meat is very tender (the cooking time depends on the size of the pork cubes). Stir in the cilantro just before serving.

4 Serve the curry with the steamed rice, and with accompaniments such as mung bean dhal and cucumber raita, if desired.

COOK'S TIPS
You can make the vindaloo marinade yourself or, if short on time, you can substitute this for about ½ cup good-quality prepared vindaloo paste.

To obtain 2 cups cooked rice you will need ⅔ cup raw rice.

G GI MEDIUM
Per serving (½ cup pork mixture over ½ cup rice)
430 Cal, 12 g fat (saturated 2.5 g),
35 g protein, 46 g carbohydrate, 3 g fiber, 16 g sugar,
95 mg sodium

Equals: 1 Nutrisystem® Dinner + 1 Fruit/Vegetable + 1 Protein + 1 Fat

Recipe: Carol Selva Rajah, Gourmet Asian Cuisine

GRILLED FISH TIKKA MAKES 4 SKEWERS

Here the fish and vegetables are threaded onto long metal skewers and then marinated in a spicy yogurt mixture. Traditionally, the tikka is cooked in an Indian clay tandoor oven, which gives it a wonderful smoky flavor, but you can cook your skewers on the grill. Preparation time: 20 minutes Marinating time: 30 minutes Cooking time: 10 minutes

FISH SKEWERS
1 – 14 oz firm white fish steak, cut into 16 chunks, about 1 in each
1 large red onion, cut into 8 wedges
½ red pepper, cut into 6 pieces, about 1 in square
½ green pepper, cut into 6 pieces, about 1 in square

YOGURT MARINADE
1 cup low-fat natural yogurt
½ onion, finely chopped
2 teaspoons finely grated ginger
2 garlic cloves, minced
1 teaspoon ground coriander
2 tablespoons lemon juice
1 tablespoon garam masala
1 teaspoon paprika
1 teaspoon chili powder, or to taste
2 tablespoons tomato paste

4 lemon wedges
saffron pilaf (page 136), to serve (optional)
cucumber raita (page 134), to serve (optional)
mung bean dhal (page 136), to serve (optional)

1 To make the yogurt marinade, combine all the ingredients in a non-metallic bowl and mix well.

2 To make the fish skewers, allow 4 fish chunks, 2 onion wedges and 3 squares of pepper (a mix of red and green look good) for each skewer. Thread the fish chunks, onion wedges and pepper squares onto the skewers in the following order: pepper, fish, onion, fish, pepper, fish, onion, fish, pepper. Place in a shallow dish that is long enough to hold the skewers. Coat the skewers with the marinade mixture, cover, and refrigerate for 30 minutes to allow the flavors to develop.

3 Heat a grill and cook the fish skewers for about 5 minutes on each side, or until the fish is cooked through and the vegetables are slightly charred on the edges.

4 Serve the fish skewers with lemon wedges for squeezing over. You may also like to serve with accompaniments such as saffron pilaf, cucumber raita and mung bean dhal.

GI LOW Ⓖ

Per serving (1 fish skewer)
190 Cal, 3.5 g fat (saturated 1 g),
25 g protein, 15 g carbohydrate, 2 g fiber, 7 g sugar,
105 mg sodium

Equals: 1 Nutrisystem® Dinner

Recipe: Carol Selva Rajah, Gourmet Asian Cuisine

SLOW-ROAST LAMB WITH CHICKPEAS SERVES 6

This recipe is perfect for a dinner party or family get-together, as everything can be prepared in advance and pulled from the oven when you are ready to eat. Potatoes are usually served with a roast but unnecessary here, as a chickpea and tomato sauce provides the starchy accompaniment. Preparation time: 15 minutes Cooking time: 2½–3 hours

4 large garlic cloves, minced
1 teaspoon ground cumin
2 tablespoons olive oil
juice of 1 lemon
freshly ground black pepper
2 lb 4 oz leg of lamb, large areas of visible fat removed
2 onions, chopped
1 cup vegetable stock
4 tablespoons tomato paste
1 – 14 oz can chopped tomatoes
1 cinnamon stick
¼ teaspoon ground cloves
1 tablespoon pure floral honey
1 – 14 oz can chickpeas, rinsed and drained

1 Preheat the oven to 325°F. Put the garlic, cumin, oil and lemon juice in a bowl, season with pepper, and mix to combine. Rub this mixture over the lamb.

2 Put the lamb in a large, non-stick baking pan over medium heat and brown the lamb on all sides. Remove from the pan and set aside.

3 Add the onions to the hot pan and fry for 4–5 minutes, or until soft and translucent. Add the stock, tomato paste, tomatoes, cinnamon, cloves and honey and mix well. Return the lamb to the pan and spoon over the sauce. Cover with a well-fitting lid or foil and roast in the oven for 2½–3 hours. Remove the lamb, set aside and keep warm, then return the pan to the stovetop. Add the chickpeas and heat through.

4 Slice the lamb and serve with the chickpea tomato sauce spooned over the top. Serve with steamed green vegetables, if desired.

ACTIVITY TIP
A balanced exercise program, including aerobic, resistance and stretching exercise, will give you the best results. Variety is also important because the body becomes efficient at anything it does repeatedly, so after a while you'll need to add something new to your exercise program.

Ⓖ GI LOW

Per serving (2 slices of lamb, ¾ cup chickpea tomato sauce)
380 Cal, 12 g fat (saturated 3 g),
40 g protein, 25 g carbohydrate, 5 g fiber, 10 g sugar,
310 mg sodium

Equals: 1 Nutrisystem® Dinner +
1 Fruit/Vegetable + 1 Fat

BARLEY RISOTTO WITH TROUT SERVES 5

Barley is one of the oldest cultivated cereals and has one of the lowest GI values of any food. It's also versatile: add pearl barley to soups and stews, fuel your day with barley porridge or make a barley risotto—all great ways to reduce the overall GI of a meal.
Preparation time: 15 minutes   Cooking time: 1 hour

1 tablespoon olive oil
1 onion, finely chopped
2 large garlic cloves, minced
2 cups (7 oz) fresh shiitake mushrooms, sliced
1 cup pearl barley
2 tablespoons barbecue sauce
2 cups hot vegetable stock
freshly ground black pepper
5 – 4 oz trout fillets
juice of ½ lemon
1 tablespoon chopped dill
lemon wedges, to serve (optional)

1 Preheat the oven to 350°F. Heat the oil in a flameproof casserole dish over medium heat and sauté the onion and garlic for about 3 minutes, or until soft. Add the mushrooms and cook for 1–2 minutes, then add the barley, barbecue sauce and hot stock. Stir well and season with pepper.

2 Cover with the lid and bake for 40–45 minutes. Place the trout fillets on top of the risotto, squeeze over the lemon juice and season with pepper. Replace the lid and cook for 15 minutes.

3 Flake the trout into large pieces and gently combine with the barley risotto. Sprinkle with the dill and serve with lemon wedges, for squeezing over, if desired. Serve with either a green salad or steamed green vegetables.

 COOK'S TIP
To reduce the cooking time, cover the barley with water in the morning and leave to soak for the day.

GI LOW Ⓖ
Per serving (1½ cups)
380 Cal, 11 g fat (saturated 2 g),
29 g protein, 42 g carbohydrate, 8 g fiber, 4 g sugar,
190 mg sodium

**Equals: Nutrisystem® Dinner +
1 Fruit/Vegetable + 1 Fat**

ROASTED PUMPKIN AND MUSHROOM LASAGNA SERVES 8

Soft layers of pumpkin, sweet potato and mushrooms, and a creamy ricotta sauce make this lasagna a memorable meal to share with family and friends. Preparation time: 30 minutes Cooking time: 1 hour

3 cups (14 oz) pumpkin, cut into ½ in cubes
3 cups (14 oz) orange sweet potato, cut into ½ in cubes
2 large sprigs rosemary
3 garlic cloves, minced
freshly ground black pepper
olive oil spray
4 cups skim milk
1 large onion, sliced
3 heaping tablespoons plain flour
1¼ cups ricotta cheese
9 oz lasagna sheets
2 cups (7 oz) mushrooms, sliced
1 scallion, sliced
½ cup reduced fat cheddar cheese, shredded

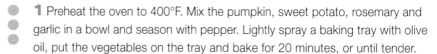

1 Preheat the oven to 400°F. Mix the pumpkin, sweet potato, rosemary and garlic in a bowl and season with pepper. Lightly spray a baking tray with olive oil, put the vegetables on the tray and bake for 20 minutes, or until tender.

2 Put the milk and onion in a saucepan over medium heat. Heat until just below boiling point, then turn off the heat and sit for 10 minutes. Mix the flour with a little water, then add to the milk, bring to a simmer and cook for 5 minutes, then add the ricotta cheese.

3 Spray a lasagna dish with olive oil. Add a layer of lasagna sheets, then a quarter of the sauce, a quarter of the baked pumpkin and sweet potato and a quarter of the mushrooms and scallions. Continue until all the lasagna sheets, vegetables and sauce are used (you will end up with four layers). Sprinkle with shredded cheese.

4 Bake for 35–45 minutes, or until cooked through and golden on top. Rest for 5 minutes before cutting. Serve with a mixed green salad, if desired.

G GI LOW

Per serving (⅛ slice)
320 Cal, 5 g fat (saturated 3 g),
20 g protein, 49 g carbohydrate, 3 g fiber, 14 g sugar,
330 mg sodium

Equals: 1 Nutrisystem® Dinner + 1 Fruit/Vegetable + 1 Fat

Recipe: Michelle Trute, Cooking with Conscience

MARINATED STEAKS WITH MEXICAN BEAN SALAD SERVES 5

Game meats, such as caribou or venison, are also a good alternative, being incredibly lean and packed with essential nutrients, including iron and zinc. Soaking time: Overnight Marinating time: 1–2 hours Preparation time: 10 minutes Cooking time: 45–50 minutes

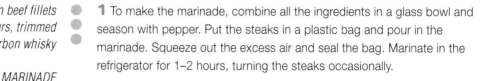

5 – 4 oz lean beef fillets
8 asparagus spears, trimmed
1 tablespoon Bourbon whisky

MARINADE
1/2 cup red wine
2 teaspoons liquid hickory smoke sauce
1 tablespoon olive oil
1 tablespoon soy sauce
1/2 teaspoon paprika
freshly ground black pepper

MEXICAN BEAN SALAD
1 1/2 cups black beans, soaked overnight in water
1 red chile, finely chopped
3 scallions, thinly sliced
1/2 red pepper, finely chopped
cayenne pepper, to taste
1 tablespoon extra-virgin olive oil

1 To make the marinade, combine all the ingredients in a glass bowl and season with pepper. Put the steaks in a plastic bag and pour in the marinade. Squeeze out the excess air and seal the bag. Marinate in the refrigerator for 1–2 hours, turning the steaks occasionally.

2 To make the Mexican bean salad, put the beans in a saucepan, cover with water and bring to a boil. Cook for 30–40 minutes, or until al dente (cooking time will vary depending on the size of the beans and their soaking time). Transfer to a bowl and allow to cool, then add the remaining salad ingredients. Cover and set aside.

3 Heat a grill or frying pan and cook the asparagus for 2–3 minutes, or until slightly browned. Remove and set aside.

4 Remove the steaks from the marinade, reserving the marinade, and pat dry with paper towels. Cook on the grill for about 3-5 minutes on each side. Lean meat should be served rare to medium-rare (overcooking the meat will leave it tough and dry).

5 Put the reserved marinade in a small saucepan and add the Bourbon. Heat gently and simmer for 4–5 minutes to reduce and thicken the sauce. To serve, spoon a little of the sauce over the steaks and serve with the warm Mexican bean salad and grilled asparagus.

GI LOW **G**

Per serving (1 fillet, 1/3 cup bean salad)
280 Cal, 10 g fat (saturated 2.5 g),
28 g protein, 16 g carbohydrate, 5 g fiber, 2 g sugar,
150 mg sodium

Equals: 1 Nutrisystem® Dinner + 1 Fruit/Vegetable + 1 Fat

Recipe: Steffan Rössner

BAKED SALMON WITH MIXED BEAN SALSA SERVES 5

In a traditional Mediterranean diet, fish would be included once or twice a week. We now know that eating fish regularly will help reduce the risk of heart disease, so aim for two or three servings a week. Preparation time: 15 minutes Cooking time: 20–30 minutes

5 – 3½ oz salmon fillets
1 lemon, halved
1 bunch cilantro, leaves picked and chopped
freshly ground black pepper

MIXED BEAN SALSA
1 – 15½ oz can three-bean mix, rinsed and drained
1 tablespoon chopped black olives
6 sun-dried tomatoes, chopped
1 red chile, finely chopped (remove the seeds for a milder taste)
1 small red onion, finely chopped
1 tablespoon olive oil
2 teaspoons balsamic vinegar

GREEN SALAD
1 tablespoon olive oil
2 teaspoons balsamic vinegar
1 teaspoon Dijon mustard
1 teaspoon pure floral honey
10 cups mixed green salad

1 Preheat the oven to 350°F. Put the salmon fillets in a baking dish, squeeze over the lemon juice, sprinkle over half of the cilantro leaves and season with plenty of pepper. Cover with foil and bake for 20–30 minutes for medium to well-done (or bake for about 15 minutes if you prefer your salmon rare).

2 Meanwhile, to make the mixed bean salsa, combine all the ingredients in a bowl. Add the remaining cilantro and mix well.

3 To make a dressing for the green salad, put the oil, vinegar, mustard and honey in a screw-top jar and shake to combine. Drizzle over the salad greens.

4 Place the salmon fillets on each plate, top with a generous spoonful of the bean salsa and serve with the green salad.

G GI LOW

Per serving (1 salmon fillet, ⅓ cup beans, 2 cups salad greens)
300 Cal, 10 g fat (saturated 1.5 g),
27 g protein, 26 g carbohydrate, 9 g fiber, 7 g sugar,
170 mg sodium

Equals: 1 Nutrisystem® Dinner + 1 Fruit/Vegetable + 1 Fat

CHICKEN PASTA WITH CARAMELIZED ONIONS SERVES 6

It's worth taking the time to roast the pepper and remove its skin before adding it to the pasta, as this makes it sweeter (the skin can be a little bitter). Preparation time: 15 minutes Cooking time: 35 minutes

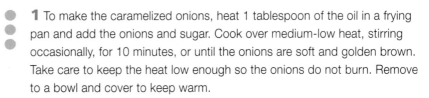

2 tablespoons olive oil
2 red onions, peeled and cut into thin wedges
2 teaspoons sugar
1 red pepper
2 chicken breast fillets (about 10½ oz), thinly sliced
4 scallions, sliced
2 teaspoons crushed garlic
1 cup evaporated low-fat milk
1 cup chicken stock
2 tablespoons sun-dried tomato pesto or tomato paste
12 oz dried pasta, such as spirals or penne
½ cup shredded basil
freshly ground black pepper

1 To make the caramelized onions, heat 1 tablespoon of the oil in a frying pan and add the onions and sugar. Cook over medium-low heat, stirring occasionally, for 10 minutes, or until the onions are soft and golden brown. Take care to keep the heat low enough so the onions do not burn. Remove to a bowl and cover to keep warm.

2 Cut the pepper into quarters lengthways and remove the seeds and stalk. Lay the pieces, skin-side up, on a lined baking tray, place under a broiler and cook for about 7 minutes, or until the skin is blackened and blistered. Using tongs, place the hot pieces of pepper in a plastic freezer bag. Twist to seal and put aside to cool slightly. When cool, remove the skin and slice the flesh into strips.

3 Meanwhile, heat the remaining tablespoon of oil in a large frying pan. Add the chicken and cook for 4–5 minutes, or until the chicken is browned and cooked through. Add the scallions and garlic and cook for 1 minute. Stir in the evaporated milk, stock, pesto and pepper strips. Bring to a boil, then reduce the heat and simmer for 1–2 minutes. Remove the chicken mixture to a bowl and cover to keep warm.

4 Cook the pasta in a large saucepan of boiling water until al dente. When the pasta is cooked, drain it and return to the saucepan. Stir in the chicken mixture and caramelized onion and heat through. Stir in the basil and season with pepper.

GI LOW

Per serving (2 oz chicken, 2 oz pasta)
400 Cal, 8 g fat (saturated 1.5 g),
23 g protein, 57 g carbohydrate, 4 g fiber, 12 g sugar,
170 mg sodium

Equals: 1 Nutrisystem® Dinner + 1 Fruit/Vegetable + 1 Protein + 1 Fat

CHICKEN TAGINE WITH SWEET POTATO, CARROTS AND PRUNES SERVES 6

The combination of ginger, cinnamon, prunes and honey gives this tagine that taste of Morocco. Serve this one-pot meal with a crispy salad and bread to mop up the juices. Preparation time: 15 minutes Cooking time: 45–50 minutes

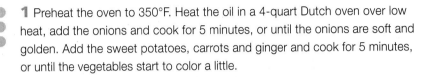

1 tablespoon olive oil
20 pearl onions
2 orange sweet potatoes (about 5 cups),
cut into bite-sized chunks
2 carrots, cut into bite-sized chunks
1 tablespoon grated ginger
12 pitted prunes
1 teaspoon ground cinnamon
1 teaspoon pure floral honey
1½ cups vegetable or chicken stock
freshly ground black pepper
4 chicken breast fillets (about 1 lb 5 oz),
skin and visible fat removed,
cut into quarters
2 tablespoons chopped cilantro leaves
2 tablespoons chopped mint

1 Preheat the oven to 350°F. Heat the oil in a 4-quart Dutch oven over low heat, add the onions and cook for 5 minutes, or until the onions are soft and golden. Add the sweet potatoes, carrots and ginger and cook for 5 minutes, or until the vegetables start to color a little.

2 Stir in the prunes, cinnamon and honey. Allow to heat through, then pour in the stock and season with pepper. Lay the chicken pieces in the liquid, then cover the dish and cook in the oven for 35–40 minutes, or until the chicken is cooked through. Stir in the cilantro and mint and serve.

ACTIVITY TIP

Dancing in some form has always been important for humans all around the globe. Find a class close to you, hit the local nightspot or simply throw on your favorite CD at home and get moving!

GI LOW
Per serving (1½ cups)
300 Cal, 6 g fat (saturated 1 g),
25 g protein, 37 g carbohydrate, 4 g fiber, 8 g sugar,
240 mg sodium

Equals: 1 Nutrisystem® Dinner + 1 Fruit/Vegetable + 1 Fat

SWEET POTATOES IN GINGER, CAYENNE AND PEANUT SAUCE SERVES 8

Savor the flavor of this robust vegetarian dish and serve with a side dish of basmati rice, or as the carb accompaniment to meat or fish. Preparation time: 20 minutes Cooking time: 45 minutes

1 tablespoon olive oil
1 large onion, roughly chopped
4 garlic cloves, minced
2 in piece ginger, finely grated
3 small sweet potatoes (6 cups), cubed
1 lb cabbage, roughly chopped
2 teaspoons paprika
1 teaspoon cayenne pepper
1 – 15½ oz can diced tomatoes
1 cup pineapple juice
½ cup smooth peanut butter
freshly ground black pepper
1 carrot, grated
1 raw beet, grated
1 banana, sliced
juice of 1 lime
2 tablespoons chopped cilantro leaves
4 cups steamed basmati rice

1 Heat the oil in a large heavy-based saucepan over medium heat and sauté the onion, garlic and ginger for 2 minutes, then add the sweet potatoes and cabbage. When the vegetables start to soften, add the paprika and cayenne. Stir to coat the vegetables in the spices. Add the tomatoes and pineapple juice. Cover and simmer for 35–40 minutes, or until the vegetables are soft.

2 Stir in the peanut butter until well combined, adding a little water if it is too thick. Season with pepper, then transfer to serving bowls.

3 Toss the carrot, beet and banana in the lime juice and scatter over the vegetables. Garnish with cilantro and serve with steamed low GI rice, if desired.

G GI LOW

Per serving (³/₄ cup with ½ cup basmati rice)
330 Cal, 10 g fat (saturated 2 g),
8 g protein, 53 g carbohydrate, 6 g fiber, 15 g sugar,
260 mg sodium

Equals: 1 Nutrisystem® Dinner +
1 Fruit/Vegetable + 1 Fat

Recipe: Chris and Carolyn Caldicott, World Food Café

CRUNCHY-TOPPED LENTIL LOAF SERVES 4–6

Lentils are one of nature's superfoods—rich in protein, fiber and B vitamins. All colors and types have a similar low GI. Serve this lentil loaf with a spicy homemade tomato salsa, or pack and take on a picnic.

Preparation time: 20 minutes Cooking time: 1¼ hours

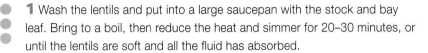

⅓ cup red lentils
½ cup green lentils
1½ cups chicken stock
1 bay leaf
1 teaspoon olive oil
1 onion, finely chopped
1 garlic clove, minced
4½ oz mushrooms, finely chopped
½ red pepper, finely chopped
½ yellow pepper, finely chopped
1½ cups loosely packed fresh
whole grain breadcrumbs
2 tablespoons chopped cilantro leaves
zest and juice of ½ lemon
2 eggs, lightly beaten
freshly ground black pepper

1 Wash the lentils and put into a large saucepan with the stock and bay leaf. Bring to a boil, then reduce the heat and simmer for 20–30 minutes, or until the lentils are soft and all the fluid has absorbed.

2 Preheat the oven to 350°F. Line a loaf pan with non-stick parchment paper.

3 Heat the oil in a saucepan or large deep frying pan and sauté the onion and garlic for 2 minutes, or until the onion is soft. Add the mushrooms and peppers and cook for 2 minutes. Remove the bay leaf and add the lentil mixture to the pan, along with the breadcrumbs (reserving about 3 tablespoons of the breadcrumbs), cilantro, lemon zest and juice, and the beaten egg. Season with pepper and mix well. The mixture should be soft, but not runny.

4 Spoon the lentils into the prepared pan, sprinkle the reserved breadcrumbs over the top, and bake for 35–40 minutes, or until firm to the touch. Remove from the oven and allow to cool in the pan for 10 minutes before turning out.

5 Serve hot or cold in thick slices with your favorite tomato salsa and a mixed green salad.

GI LOW

Per serving (⅙ loaf)
200 Cal, 4.5 g fat (saturated 1 g),
13 g protein, 29 g carbohydrate, 5 g fiber, 4 g sugar,
190 mg sodium

Equals: 1 Nutrisystem® Dinner + 1 Fat

Recipe: Isobel McMillan

ROAST LAMB AND VEGETABLES WITH THYME AND ROSEMARY SERVES 8

This is your traditional roast with a flavorsome, and healthy, Mediterranean twist. Roasting vegetables brings out their natural sweetness and is an easy way of serving a great array. Preparation time: 20 minutes Chilling time: 6 hours or overnight Cooking time: 1 hour

2 tablespoons roughly chopped thyme
3 tablespoons olive oil
2 lb 4 oz boneless leg of lamb
5 sprigs thyme, each sprig broken into 3 pieces
3 sweet potatoes (about 2 lb 12 oz), cut into 1¼ in chunks
6 zucchini (about 1 lb 2 oz), cut in half lengthways
3 large red onions, each cut into 8 wedges
1 red pepper, cut lengthways into 12 slices
3 sprigs rosemary
3 garlic cloves, each cut into 5 slices
2 tablespoons lemon juice

1 Combine the chopped thyme and 1 tablespoon of the oil in a small bowl. Put the lamb into a large glass dish and use your hands to coat the lamb in the thyme mixture.

2 Roll up the lamb and tie with kitchen string to keep the shape and ensure the lamb cooks evenly. Then, using a sharp knife, cut 15 evenly spaced slits, about ¾ in deep and ½ in long, into the top of the lamb. Insert a sprig of thyme into each slit. Cover with plastic wrap and refrigerate for at least 6 hours or overnight.

3 Preheat the oven to 350°F. Put all of the vegetables together in a large roasting pan and scatter over the leaves from the rosemary. Drizzle with 1 tablespoon of the oil and toss gently to coat. Place the lamb on top of the vegetables. Insert a slice of garlic into each slit with the thyme.

4 Put the lemon juice and the remaining tablespoon of oil in a screw-top jar and shake to combine. Drizzle over the lamb. Roast in the oven, basting with the pan juices occasionally, for 50 minutes (rare) or 60 minutes (medium). Turn off the oven. Transfer the lamb to a plate, cover with foil and set aside for 10 minutes to rest. Return the vegetables to the oven to keep warm until the lamb is ready to be sliced and served.

Ⓖ GI LOW

Per serving (3 oz lamb, ⅓ cup potatoes, 1 cup vegetables)
390 Cal, 11 g fat (saturated 2.5 g),
31 g protein, 44 g carbohydrate, 7 g fiber, 11 g sugar,
180 mg sodium

Equals: 1 Nutrisystem® Dinner + 1 Fruit/Vegetable + 1 Protein + 1 Fat

PORK WITH HONEY GLAZED APPLES SERVES 4

Lentils gently simmered in stock until they are mushy make a delicious low GI mash for all sorts of meaty mains and are very quick and easy to prepare.

Preparation time: 15 minutes Cooking time: 40–45 minutes

olive oil spray
4 – 4 oz pork loin steaks, butterflied,
or medallions
2 teaspoons poly- or monounsaturated
margarine
2 teaspoons olive oil
2 green apples, cored and cut into
1/4 in thick slices
1 tablespoon pure floral honey
1 tablespoon lemon juice
2 cups steamed green beans, to serve

RED LENTIL MASH
2/3 cup split red lentils
1 bay leaf
1 cup vegetable stock

1 Spray a non-stick frying pan with olive oil and heat over medium–high heat. Add the pork to the pan and cook for 4–5 minutes on each side, or until lightly browned and cooked to your liking. Transfer to a plate and cover to keep warm.

2 Add the margarine and oil to the pan and reduce the heat to medium–low. Add the apple slices and cook for about 7 minutes, stirring and turning occasionally, until the apples begin to brown. Add the honey and lemon juice and stir to coat the apples. Cook for 2 minutes, or until heated through.

3 To make the red lentil mash, put the lentils and bay leaf in a saucepan and add the stock. Bring to a boil, then reduce to a simmer and cook for 20–25 minutes, stirring occasionally (add extra water if the mixture becomes too dry). Cook until the lentils are soft and mushy.

4 Serve a scoop of the lentil mash on individual plates, top with the pork and apples and drizzle over the pan juices. Serve with steamed green beans.

ACTIVITY TIP
Research has shown that just 30 minutes of moderate intensity exercise each day can help to improve your health. If you prefer, you can break this down to two sessions of 15 minutes, or even three sessions of 10 minutes, and you will still see some benefits.

GI LOW

Per serving (1 pork medallion, 1/2 cup apple,
2 Tbsp lentil mash, 1/2 cup green beans)
480 Cal, 13 g fat (saturated 4 g),
36 g protein, 57 g carbohydrate, 14 g fiber, 19 g sugar,
470 mg sodium

**Equals: 1 Nutrisystem® Dinner + 1 Fruit/Vegetable +
1 Vegetable + 1 Protein + 1 Fat**

BEEF FAJITAS SERVES 6

This recipe makes enough for three rolls for each person. Serve the fajitas accompanied with your choice of grated cheese, shredded lettuce, guacamole, yogurt, tomato salsa and refried beans.

Preparation time: 15 minutes Cooking time: 15 minutes

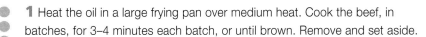

2 tablespoons olive oil
1 lb 2 oz rump steak, thinly sliced
1 red onion, sliced
1 red pepper, sliced
1 yellow pepper, sliced
1–2 jalapeño chiles, seeded and finely chopped
½ teaspoon chili powder
2 teaspoons sweet paprika
1 teaspoon ground cumin
1 teaspoon ground coriander
juice of 1 lime
2 tablespoons tomato paste
2 tablespoons chopped cilantro leaves
12 soft flour tortillas

1 Heat the oil in a large frying pan over medium heat. Cook the beef, in batches, for 3–4 minutes each batch, or until brown. Remove and set aside.

2 Add the onion, peppers and chiles and cook for 3 minutes. Stir in the chili powder, paprika, cumin, ground coriander, lime juice and tomato paste. Return all the meat to the pan and cook for 2–3 minutes, or until heated through. Stir in the cilantro leaves.

3 Heat the tortillas following the package instructions, either in the microwave for 30 seconds, or wrap in foil and warm in the oven for a few minutes. Spoon a portion of the beef mixture onto a plate with a tortilla. To eat, place some of the beef mixture on one side of a tortilla, add accompaniments of your choice, and roll up.

G GI LOW

Per serving (2 fajitas)
350 Cal, 13 g fat (saturated 3 g),
24 g protein, 34 g carbohydrate, 3 g fiber, 4 g sugar,
430 mg sodium

**Equals: 1 Nutrisystem® Dinner +
1 Fruit/Vegetable + 1 Fat**

CHICKEN BREASTS WITH LENTIL MASH SERVES 6

These chicken breasts are stuffed with a creamy mix of feta cheese, spinach and semi-dried tomatoes and served on spicy lentil mash with a mixed green salad to make a meal where everyone will be coming back for more …

Preparation time: 20 minutes Cooking time: 1 hour

6 chicken breast fillets (about 1 lb 5 oz total), skin and visible fat removed

STUFFING
3 cups baby spinach leaves
1/4 cup semi-dried tomatoes
1/3 cup reduced fat feta cheese, crumbled
1 tablespoon low-fat cream cheese
freshly ground black pepper

GREEN LENTIL MASH
1 cup green lentils
1/4 teaspoon ground turmeric
1 tablespoon olive oil
1 onion, finely chopped
2 garlic cloves, minced
juice of 1/2 lemon
freshly ground black pepper

1 To make a stuffing for the chicken, put the spinach, semi-dried tomatoes, feta cheese and cream cheese in the bowl of a food processor. Season with pepper, then roughly blend. Be careful not to overprocess; the mixture should be quite coarse.

2 Preheat the oven to 400°F. Slice open the chicken breasts lengthways to create a pocket. Fill the pockets with the stuffing. Place the chicken in a baking dish, cover with foil and bake for 30 minutes, or until cooked through and golden brown.

3 Meanwhile, to make the green lentil mash, put the lentils in a saucepan over medium heat, cover with water, and add the turmeric. Bring to a boil, then reduce the heat to a simmer and cook, partially covered, for about 30 minutes, or until the lentils are soft.

4 Toward the end of cooking, heat the oil in a saucepan and fry the onion and garlic for 3–4 minutes, or until the onion is soft. Add the lentils, lemon juice and season with plenty of pepper.

5 Serve the lentil mash topped with the stuffed chicken breast. Serve with a mixed green salad or steamed vegetables.

GI LOW

Per serving (1 stuffed chicken breast, 2 Tbsp lentil mash)
280 Cal, 7 g fat (saturated 2 g),
30 g protein, 24 g carbohydrate, 6 g fiber, 3 g sugar,
300 mg sodium

Equals: 1 Nutrisystem® Dinner +
1 Fruit/Vegetable + 1 Fat

DESSERTS AND SWEET TREATS

BEING ON A LOW GI DIET DOESN'T MEAN WE HAVE TO SKIP DESSERT. IN FACT, MANY OF THE INGREDIENTS USED IN DESSERTS, SUCH AS FRUIT AND DAIRY PRODUCTS, HAVE A LOW GI. THEY MAKE A VALUABLE CONTRIBUTION TO OUR FRUIT AND DAIRY INTAKE AND, BEING CARBOHYDRATE-RICH, ADD TO OUR FEELING OF FULLNESS.

HONEY BANANA CUPS SERVES 2

Preparation time: 5 minutes

1 cup low-fat honey-flavored yogurt
1 large banana, just ripe, peeled and sliced
2 passionfruit

1 Spoon the yogurt into two small cups, dividing evenly between them. Divide the banana between the two cups and spoon the passionfruit over the top.

COOK'S TIP
Unlike most other fruit, bananas contain both sugars and starch. The less ripe the banana, the lower its GI. As the banana ripens, the starch turns to sugars and the GI increases.

G GI LOW

Per serving (³/₄ cup)
160 Cal, 2 g fat (saturated 1 g),
6 g protein, 31 g carbohydrate, 3 g fiber, 22 g sugar,
85 mg sodium

Equals: 1 Nutrisystem® Snack

ITALIAN STRAWBERRIES SERVES 4

Preparation time: 5 minutes

4 cups strawberries, sliced
2 tablespoons balsamic vinegar
2 tablespoons sugar
small mint leaves, to garnish
8 small scoops (1 cup) low-fat ice cream
or frozen yogurt, to serve

1 Place the strawberries in a bowl. Pour over the vinegar, sprinkle with the sugar and toss to combine. Divide the strawberries between four bowls and garnish with the mint leaves. Serve with a couple of scoops of ice cream or frozen yogurt.

G GI LOW

Per serving (¹/₄ cup ice cream, 1 cup strawberry mixture)
140 Cal, 1.5 g fat (saturated .5 g),
3 g protein, 31 g carbohydrate, 4 g fiber, 25 g sugar,
25 mg sodium

Equals: 1 Nutrisystem® Snack

Recipe: Steffan Rössner

Right: Honey banana cups

FRESH PLUM AND RICOTTA STRUDEL SERVES 8

Plums and other blue-red fruit, such as cherries, blueberries and cranberries, are rich in a particular type of antioxidant known as anthocyanins. Here's a low-fat version of the strudel Catherine Saxelby makes, but using plums instead of apples.
Preparation time: 20 minutes Cooking time: 45 minutes

2 tablespoons poly- or monounsaturated margarine
1/2 cup fresh whole wheat breadcrumbs
1/3 cup soft brown sugar
1/2 teaspoon ground cinnamon
6 fresh plums or 1 – 15 oz can plums, drained well
6 sheets filo pastry
olive oil spray
1/2 cup reduced fat ricotta cheese

1 Melt the margarine in a saucepan over medium heat. Add the breadcrumbs and sugar, reserving 2 teaspoons sugar, and cook for 15 minutes, stirring to break up any lumps. Remove from the heat and stir in the cinnamon. Allow to cool.

2 Halve the plums, remove the stones, and thinly slice the flesh.

3 Preheat the oven to 375°F. Lightly grease a baking tray. Lay two sheets of filo pastry on top of each other. Spray the top sheet with olive oil, then sprinkle over one-third of the crumb mixture. Top with two more filo sheets, spray the top sheet with oil, then sprinkle over another third of the crumbs. Top with the remaining two sheets, spray with oil, then sprinkle over the remaining crumbs.

4 Spread the ricotta along the edge of the pastry. Arrange the plums on top and sprinkle with the reserved sugar. Roll up the pastry, as for a Swiss roll, tucking in the edges as you roll. Carefully transfer the roll to the prepared baking tray. Spray the top with oil and bake for 10 minutes, then reduce the heat to 350°F and bake for 20 minutes, or until the pastry is crisp and brown. Serve warm with low-fat vanilla ice cream, if desired.

Catherine Saxelby is Australia's most dynamic nutritionist and food commentator who understands the demands of today's busy world and the complexity of food issues. The author of seven books, she is also Nutrition Editor for *Table* magazine and has written many articles on all aspects of food, fat loss and special diets in a career spanning 20 years.

GI LOW Ⓖ
Per serving (1/8 roll)
150 Cal, 4.5 g fat (saturated 1 g),
3 g protein, 25 g carbohydrate, 2 g fiber, 13 g sugar
115 mg sodium

Equals: 1 Nutrisystem® Snack

CHOCOLATE APPLESAUCE CUPCAKES MAKES 18

These cupcakes are light, moist and very delicious. Although the estimated GI is medium, they have a relatively small amount of carbohydrate per cake. They are also low in saturated fat, which makes them a good choice as an occasional indulgence.
Preparation time: 15 minutes Cooking time: 25 minutes

½ cup reduced fat poly- or monounsaturated margarine or butter
¾ cup sugar
2 eggs
½ cup cocoa powder
1½ cups applesauce
1¾ cups unbleached all-purpose flour
1 teaspoon baking powder
1 teaspoon baking soda
½ teaspoon salt

1 Preheat the oven to 350°F. Grease and flour 18 holes of two 12-cup muffin pans.

2 Cream the margarine and sugar in a deep mixing bowl with electric beaters for 1–2 minutes, or until pale. Add the eggs and cocoa powder and mix until smooth. Fold in the applesauce.

3 Combine the flour, baking powder, baking soda and the salt in a small mixing bowl. Stir the dry ingredients into the egg mixture and gently mix to combine; do not overmix.

4 Spoon the mixture into the prepared holes, filling each one half to three-quarters full. Bake for 22–25 minutes, or until a wooden pick inserted into the center comes out clean. Cool a little before removing the cakes from the pans.

Ⓖ GI MEDIUM
Per serving (1 cake)
140 Cal, 4 g fat (saturated 1 g),
4 g protein, 26 g carbohydrate, 3 g fiber, 13 g sugar
210 mg sodium

Equals: 1 Nutrisystem® Snack

Recipe: Johanna Burani

SYRUPY ORANGES WITH YOGURT SERVES 4

So the only fruit you have is oranges? You can still make a delicious dessert. Not only that, you'll also be boosting your fruit intake and enjoying all the health benefits of a single orange.

Preparation time: 10 minutes Cooking time: 15 minutes

juice of 1 orange
2 tablespoons sugar
2 large oranges, peeled, pith removed
1 tablespoon brandy or Cointreau™ liqueur (optional)
1 cup peach and passionfruit frozen yogurt
4 slices almond bread

1 Combine the orange juice, sugar and ¼ cup water in a frying pan. Stir over medium heat until the sugar dissolves. Reduce the heat to low and simmer, without stirring, for 10–12 minutes to reduce the syrup.

2 Cut the peeled oranges into slices about ½ in thick and add to the syrup in the pan. Add the brandy or liqueur, bring to a simmer for 3 minutes.

3 Spoon the oranges into bowls and pour over the syrup. Top with a scoop of frozen yogurt and serve with the almond bread.

 COOK'S TIP
Almond bread is a very thin, slightly sweet crispbread containing whole almonds. It is available in the gourmet section of supermarkets.

GI LOW

Per serving (¼ orange mixture, 1 slice almond bread, ¼ cup frozen yogurt)
190 Cal, 2 g fat (saturated 1 g),
3 g protein, 28 g carbohydrate, 2 g fiber, 17 g sugar
80 mg sodium

Equals: 1 Nutrisystem® Snack

CHOCOLATE MOUSSE WITH BERRIES SERVES 6

This is a delectable version of a traditionally high fat favorite. It can be made up to 2 days ahead and is very easy to prepare. For the best results, use a good-quality cocoa powder.

Preparation time: 10 minutes Cooking time: 5 minutes Chilling time: 2–3 hours

¼ cup cocoa powder
2 teaspoons unflavored gelatin
½ cup sugar
1½ cups evaporated skim milk
½ cup light cream
1 cup strawberries or raspberries, to serve

1 Sift the cocoa into a saucepan, then stir in the gelatin and sugar. Stir in about ¼ cup of the milk, stirring to form a smooth paste. Put the saucepan over medium heat and stir for about 3 minutes to dissolve the sugar and gelatin, then gradually stir in the remaining milk. Heat until the liquid is hot but not boiling, stirring occasionally.

2 Remove from the heat, stir in the cream, then divide the mixture between six ½ cup dessert glasses or ramekins. Chill until set.

3 Serve with the fresh berries.

ACTIVITY TIP
Working with a personal trainer can be a great way to improve your health and fitness. A good trainer will design an exercise program tailored to your needs and fitness level, as well as provide motivation and support. Many trainers now offer services for a reasonable rate and you can choose to use a health club or train at home or outdoors.

G GI LOW
Per serving (1 dessert cup)
160 Cal, 5 g fat (saturated 3 g),
9 g protein, 27 g carbohydrate, 5 g fiber, 21 g sugar
85 mg sodium

Equals: 1 Nutrisystem® Snack

FRUIT SOUFFLÉ SERVES 4

This soufflé is made with semolina, which has a low GI of 55. Semolina is a coarse grain made from the first millings of the creamy yellow endosperm from wheat grain (the finer grain, when milled from durum wheat, is used to make pasta). Here the semolina is cooked with low GI fruit to make a delicious, hot soufflé. Preparation time: 15 minutes Cooking time: 30 minutes

1 lb mixed fresh fruit, such as apples,
rhubarb and/or berries
2 tablespoons soft brown sugar
2½ cups skim milk
5 tablespoons semolina
1 egg, separated
ground nutmeg

1 Preheat the oven to 350°F. Chop the fruit (except if using berries) and place in a saucepan with 1 tablespoon of the sugar and ¼ cup water. Bring to a boil, then reduce the heat, cover and simmer for 5–10 minutes, or until the fruit is soft. Spoon the fruit into a 5 cup-capacity baking dish or into four 1 cup-capacity soufflé dishes.

2 Put the milk in a saucepan and heat until just coming to a boil. Sprinkle the semolina and the remaining sugar over the milk. Cook, stirring, until the mixture thickens, then continue to cook for 1 minute. Remove the pan from the heat, stir in the egg yolk and allow to cool slightly.

3 Whisk the egg white until stiff peaks form, then fold into the semolina. Spoon the semolina mixture over the fruit and sprinkle with the nutmeg. Bake for 20 minutes, or until the soufflé has risen and is golden. Serve hot.

GI LOW Ⓖ
Per serving (1 dessert cup)
190 Cal, 2 g fat (saturated .5 g),
10 g protein, 34 g carbohydrate, 3 g fiber, 20 g sugar,
90 mg sodium

Equals: 1 Nutrisystem® Snack

APRICOT OAT MUNCHIES MAKES ABOUT 24

Need a quick snack between meals? Then make a batch of these delicious apricot and oat munchies. Store in an airtight container and use for school lunches, or bake these healthy cookies and serve on festive occasions.

Preparation time: 15 minutes Cooking time: 12–15 minutes

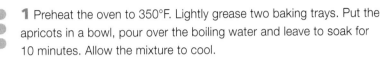

1 cup dried apricots, chopped
1/3 cup boiling water
1 cup rolled oats
1 cup unbleached all-purpose flour, sifted
1/2 cup oat bran
1/2 cup soft brown sugar
1/2 cup chopped walnuts
1/2 teaspoon baking powder
1/2 teaspoon ground cinnamon
1/2 teaspoon ground nutmeg
2 egg whites
3 tablespoons olive oil

1 Preheat the oven to 350°F. Lightly grease two baking trays. Put the apricots in a bowl, pour over the boiling water and leave to soak for 10 minutes. Allow the mixture to cool.

2 Combine the oats, flour, oat bran, sugar, walnuts, baking powder and spices in a large bowl.

3 Beat the egg whites until stiff peaks form, fold into the cooled apricot mixture, then add the oil. Mix into the dry ingredients.

4 Drop spoonfuls of the mixture onto the prepared baking trays, then bake for 12–15 minutes, or until light brown. Leave for 5 minutes before lifting off the tray and placing on a wire rack to cool. Store in an airtight container.

Ⓖ GI MEDIUM

Per serving (1 cookie)
110 Cal, 4 g fat (saturated 0 g),
2 g protein, 17 g carbohydrate, 1 g fiber, 3 g sugar
20 mg sodium

Equals: 1 Nutrisystem® Snack

Recipe: Catherine Saxelby, Eating for the Healthy Heart

SCOTTISH OATCAKES MAKES 35

Traditional oatcakes are made using lard or butter, both full of the saturated fats that we are recommending you cut down on.
This recipe uses an unsaturated alternative instead of butter and the result is an equally delicious but altogether healthier oatcake.
Preparation time: 15 minutes Chilling time: 20 minutes Cooking time: 15–20 minutes

1⅓ cups coarse oatmeal
½ cup whole wheat self-rising flour,
plus extra for dusting
¼ teaspoon sea salt
½ cup poly- or monounsaturated
margarine, chilled
2 tablespoons chilled water

TOPPINGS
low-fat ricotta cheese
sliced strawberries, or slices of fresh
or dried figs

1 Combine the oatmeal, flour, sea salt and margarine in the bowl of a food processor and process until the mixture resembles coarse breadcrumbs, then slowly add the chilled water until the mixture forms a stiff dough. Stop at this point, even if you haven't used all of the water.

2 Put the dough in a plastic bag and in the freezer for about 20 minutes. Preheat the oven to 350°F.

3 Remove the dough from the bag and roll out on a floured board to ⅛ in thick. Cut into rounds about 1½ in in diameter, place on a non-stick baking tray and bake for 15–20 minutes, or until golden. Transfer to a wire rack to cool.

4 To make the topping for the oatcakes, put a teaspoon of ricotta on each and top with either a sliced strawberry or a slice of fig.

COOK'S TIPS
Scottish oatcakes are also a delicious substitute for bread when served with soups and salads. Cut them into slightly larger rounds, about 2½ in in diameter, if serving with soup.

G GI LOW
Per serving (2 oatcakes with 1 tsp topping each
and 1 sliced strawberry or dried fig)
100 Cal, 6 g fat (saturated 1 g),
3 g protein, 10 g carbohydrate, 2 g fiber, 1 g sugar
105 mg sodium

Equals: 1 Nutrisystem® Snack

Recipe: Judy Davie, The Food Coach

APPLE AND STRAWBERRY CRUMBLE SERVES 6

Crumbles are real comfort food. Making the "crumble" with rolled oats keeps the GI low and the fiber high, and the strawberries are rich in vitamin C and protective antioxidants.

Preparation time: 20 minutes Cooking time: 15 minutes

*3 cooking apples, such as Granny Smiths,
peeled, cored and sliced
2 tablespoons pure floral honey
1²/₃ cups strawberries, hulled and halved
1 cup rolled oats
2 tablespoons soft brown sugar
¹/₂ teaspoon ground cinnamon
2 tablespoons canola margarine, melted*

1 Preheat the oven to 400°F. Lightly grease a medium baking dish with margarine.

2 Put the apples, honey and 2 tablespoons water in a saucepan. Bring to a boil, then reduce the heat to low, cover and simmer for 3–4 minutes, or until the apples have softened a little. Remove from the heat and stir in the strawberries. Spoon the mixture into the baking dish.

3 Put the oats in a food processor and process until the mixture is coarse. Combine the oats in a bowl with the sugar, cinnamon and margarine. Mix together and spoon evenly over the fruit.

4 Bake for 15–20 minutes, or until the crumble is crisp and golden. Serve with 6–8 oz nonfat yogurt, if desired.

ACTIVITY TIP
Develop an after-dinner walking habit with your partner or a good friend.

GI LOW
Per serving (¹/₂ cup crumble)
170 Cal, 5 g fat (saturated 1 g),
3 g protein, 30 g carbohydrate, 3 g fiber, 16 g sugar
35 mg sodium

Equals: 1 Nutrisystem® Snack

CHERRY OAT CRUNCHIES MAKES 42

Who doesn't love cookies? How about cookies that your body will love too? Add them to packed lunches, or serve with a glass of milk after school or in the evening.

Preparation time: 15 minutes Cooking time: 15 minutes

olive oil spray
¼ cup soft brown sugar
¼ cup pure floral honey
½ cup canola margarine or butter
2 eggs
½ teaspoon baking soda
½ tablespoon vanilla extract
1 cup unbleached all-purpose flour
2 cups rolled oats
20 fresh cherries, pitted and roughly chopped
½ cup roughly chopped walnuts
2 cups bran or oat flakes cereal, crushed

1 Preheat the oven to 350°F. Lightly spray two baking trays with olive oil.

2 Put the sugar, honey, margarine, eggs, baking soda and vanilla extract in a large mixing bowl. Beat on medium speed for 2 minutes. Fold in the flour, oats, cherries, walnuts and crushed bran flakes. Mix thoroughly.

3 Drop spoonfuls of the mixture onto the prepared baking trays, spacing them about 2 in apart. Bake for 15 minutes, or until light brown. Leave for 5 minutes before lifting off the tray and placing on a wire rack to cool. Store in an airtight container.

COOK'S TIP
Instead of cherries, you can try other fresh fruit in season such as berries, or substitute with ½ cup chopped dried apricots.

G GI LOW
Per serving (2 cookies)
160 Cal, 7 g fat (saturated 1 g),
4 g protein, 21 g carbohydrate, 2 g fiber, 7 g sugar
85 mg sodium

Equals: 1 Nutrisystem® Snack

Recipe: Johanna Burani

BERRY AND VANILLA CRÈME DESSERT SERVES 4

This is a delicious, simple dessert that can be made with fresh berries in summer—strawberries, blueberries and blackberries—or frozen berries when they are out of season. Berries not only have a low GI but are also incredibly rich in disease-fighting antioxidants.
Preparation time: 15 minutes Marinating time: 15 minutes

VANILLA CREME
½ cup low-fat cream cheese,
at room temperature
4 tablespoons low-fat sour cream
4 teaspoons confectioners' sugar
1 teaspoon vanilla extract

juice of 1 orange
1 tablespoon soft brown sugar
1 tablespoon sweet wine
1¼ cups mixed fresh or
frozen berries
4 lady fingers

1 To make the vanilla crème, put the cream cheese and sour cream in a mixing bowl and stir with a wooden spoon to combine. Sift in the confectioners' sugar, add the vanilla extract and stir well to combine.

2 Combine the orange juice, sugar and wine in a bowl, then add the berries and leave to marinate for 15 minutes.

3 Choose four small 1 cup glasses with a wide base. Cut a lady finger to cover the base of each glass. Add a spoonful of berries and a drizzle of marinade over the cookie base, then top with a spoonful of vanilla crème. Top with another layer of lady finger, the berries, a little more marinade, and finish with the vanilla crème. Chill until ready to serve.

GI LOW Ⓖ
Per serving (1 lady finger, ⅓ cup berries, ¼ cup cream)
190 Cal, 9 g fat (saturated 6 g),
5 g protein, 21 g carbohydrate, 4 g fiber, 16 g sugar
144 mg sodium

Equals: 1 Nutrisystem® Snack

GRAPEFRUIT GRANITA SERVES 6

This refreshing, citrusy granita is light and flavorsome and the perfect end to a heavy or spicy meal. To allow adequate time for the granita to freeze, it is best to prepare this recipe a day ahead.

Preparation time: 5 minutes Cooking time: 5 minutes Freezing time: 5½ hours

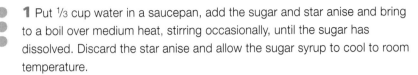

½ cup sugar
2 whole star anise
2½ cups fresh pink grapefruit juice

1 Put ⅓ cup water in a saucepan, add the sugar and star anise and bring to a boil over medium heat, stirring occasionally, until the sugar has dissolved. Discard the star anise and allow the sugar syrup to cool to room temperature.

2 Put the grapefruit juice in a bowl and stir in the cooled sugar syrup. Pour the mixture into a 13 x 9 in baking dish. Cover tightly with plastic wrap, put the dish in the freezer and freeze for about 45 minutes, or until the mixture is icy around the edge of the dish. Using a fork, scrape the edges to distribute the frozen portions evenly. Cover and freeze again for another 45 minutes, or until the mixture is icy around the edges and the overall texture is slushy. Use the fork to distribute the frozen portions evenly. Cover and return to the freezer for about 3 hours, or until frozen solid.

3 Remove from the freezer. Using a fork, scrape the granita down the length of the pan, forming icy flakes. Return to the freezer for at least 1 hour, for the final freezing. To serve, scoop the flaked granita into tall goblets or parfait glasses. When served, the granita should look like a fluffy pile of dry pink crystals.

G GI LOW
Per serving (⅙ recipe)
110 Cal, 0 g fat (saturated 0 g),
1 g protein, 28 g carbohydrate, 0 g fiber, 19 g sugar
0 mg sodium

Equals: 1 Nutrisystem® Snack

Recipe: Emma Pemberton

BASIC RECIPES

CHERMOULA SPICE MIX

½ onion, finely chopped
1 teaspoon finely chopped cilantro leaves
2 teaspoons finely chopped parsley
1 garlic clove, minced
3 teaspoons ground cumin
2 teaspoons mild paprika
1 teaspoon turmeric
pinch of cayenne pepper
salt and freshly ground black pepper

1 Combine all the ingredients and set aside to allow the flavors to develop. Use as a rub for meat or poultry before roasting or barbecuing.

MAKES ABOUT ⅓ CUP

Equals: Free–Unlimited
Recipe: Liz and Ian Hemphill, Herbies Spices

VINDALOO CURRY POWDER

6 teaspoons chili powder, to taste
4 teaspoons white poppy seeds
3 teaspoons ground cumin
2 teaspoons mild paprika
1 teaspoon ground cinnamon
1 teaspoon ground ginger
½ teaspoon amchur powder
½ teaspoon freshly ground black pepper
¼ teaspoon ground cloves
pinch ground star anise

1 Combine all the ingredients and mix thoroughly. Store in an airtight container.

MAKES ABOUT ⅔ CUP

Equals: Free–Unlimited
Recipe: Liz and Ian Hemphill, Herbies Spices

HARISSA

10 teaspoons chopped, dried red chiles
   or dried chile flakes
3 teaspoons minced garlic
3 teaspoons sweet paprika
2 teaspoons caraway seeds
2 teaspoons coriander seeds
1 teaspoon cumin seeds, dry-roasted
1 teaspoon salt
6 spearmint leaves, finely chopped
3 teaspoons olive oil

1 Soak the chiles in 10 teaspoons (1¾ fl oz) hot water for 15 minutes (do not drain off the water).

2 Crush the remaining ingredients (except the oil) using a mortar and pestle, then add to the soaked chiles in the bowl. Mix to combine. Add the oil, a little at a time, mixing to form a thick paste (you may not need to use all of the oil). Store, covered, in the refrigerator and use within 4 weeks. This Tunisian harissa blend is fairly fiery, so use with caution.

MAKES ABOUT ½ CUP; 1 SERVING: 1 TBSP

Equals: Free
Recipe: Liz and Ian Hemphill, Herbies Spices

CUCUMBER RAITA

1 cup low-fat natural yogurt
1 small cucumber, peeled and seeded,
   finely chopped
½ bunch cilantro, leaves
   picked and chopped

1 Combine all the ingredients in a serving bowl. Cover and refrigerate until needed.

MAKES ABOUT 1 CUP; 1 SERVING: 2 TBSP

Equals: Free
Recipe: Carol Selva Rajah, Gourmet Asian Cuisine

HUMMUS

1 – 14 oz can chickpeas, drained (liquid reserved)
½ cup tahini
2 garlic cloves, minced
juice of 1 lemon
¼ teaspoon salt and freshly ground black pepper, to taste

1 Combine all the ingredients in a food processor and blend, adding just enough of the reserved chickpea liquid to make a smooth paste. Serve in a bowl. Garnish with a drizzle of olive oil, chopped parsley, pine nuts and a sprinkle of paprika, if desired.

MAKES 2 CUPS

GI LOW
Per serving (2 Tbsp)
140 Cal, 11 g fat (saturated 1 g), 6 g protein, 5 g carbohydrate, 4 g fiber, 345 mg sodium

Equals: 1 Carbohydrate + 1 Fat

TABBOULI

1 cup bulgur wheat
1 cup finely chopped flat-leaf parsley
4 small scallions, finely chopped
1 tomato, finely chopped
2 tablespoons lemon juice
2 tablespoons olive oil
¼ teaspoon salt and freshly ground black pepper

1 Put the bulgur wheat in a bowl, cover with boiling water and soak for 20–30 minutes. Drain well and roll the grains in a clean, lint-free kitchen towel to squeeze out the excess water. Combine the bulgur wheat, parsley, scallion and tomato in a bowl.

2 Combine the lemon juice, oil, salt and pepper in a screw-top jar and shake well. Pour over the tabbouli and toss lightly to combine. Tabbouli will keep for 2 days, covered, in the refrigerator.

SERVES 8

GI LOW
Per serving (⅓ cup)
100 Cal, 4 g fat (saturated .5 g), 3 g protein, 15 g carbohydrate, 4 g fiber, 1 g sugar, 80 mg sodium

Equals: 1 Carbohydrate + 1 Fat

SAFFRON PILAF

1½ cups basmati rice
½ teaspoon saffron threads
1 tablespoon boiling water
1 tablespoon olive oil
3 scallions, sliced
½ red pepper, chopped
2 garlic cloves, minced
2½ cups reduced sodium chicken stock
½ cup frozen peas, defrosted
¼ cup raisins
¼ cup slivered almonds, toasted

1 Rinse the rice under cold water. Drain and set aside. Place the saffron threads in a small bowl and pour over the boiling water. Set aside to allow the color to infuse.

2 Heat the oil in a large saucepan. Cook the scallions, pepper and garlic for 2 minutes. Add the rice, stock, saffron and its soaking water, and bring to a boil. Reduce the heat to low, cover and simmer for 10–12 minutes, stirring from time to time, or until the rice is just tender.

3 Remove from the heat and stir in the peas, raisins and almonds. Cover and set aside for 5 minutes before serving.

SERVES 8

Ⓖ GI MEDIUM
Per serving (½ cup)
190 Cal, 3.5 g fat (saturated 0 g), 4 g protein,
37 g carbohydrate, 2 g fiber, 1 g sugar, 30 mg sodium

Equals: 2 Carbohydrate + 1 Fat

MUNG BEAN DHAL

1 cup dried whole mung beans
¼ teaspoon turmeric
½ teaspoon salt
1 tablespoon olive oil
½ onion, chopped
2 garlic cloves, minced
1–2 green chiles, finely chopped (remove the seeds for a milder taste)
1 bunch cilantro, leaves picked and chopped

1 Cover the mung beans with 3½ cups water and bring to a boil. Reduce the heat, add the turmeric and simmer for 40–50 minutes, or until the beans are tender. Add the salt and turn off the heat.

2 Heat the oil in a small non-stick frying pan over medium heat and sauté the onion and garlic until brown. Add the chiles and fry for 30 seconds, then tip the onion and garlic into the saucepan with the mung beans. Cover with the lid and allow the flavors to develop. Before serving, stir in the cilantro.

SERVES 4

Ⓖ GI LOW
Per serving (⅓ cup)
220 Cal, 4 g fat (saturated .5 g), 13 g protein,
35 g carbohydrate, 9 g fiber, 5 g sugar, 310 mg sodium

Equals: 2 Carbohydrate + 1 Fat
Recipe: Isobel McMillan

YOUR LOW GI FOODS

To make easy low GI choices, you'll need to stock the right foods. Here are ideas for what to keep in your pantry, refrigerator and freezer. These foods have optimum flavor and nutritional value and work well, in moderation, in a low GI diet.

WHAT TO KEEP IN YOUR PANTRY

ASIAN SAUCES* Hoi sin, oyster, soy and fish sauces are a good basic range.

BARLEY One of the oldest cultivated cereals, barley is very nutritious and high in soluble fiber. Look for products such as pearl barley to use in soups, stews and pilafs.

BLACK PEPPER Buy freshly ground pepper or grind your own peppercorns.

BREAD Low GI options include grainy, stone-ground whole grain, pumpernickel, sourdough, English-style muffins, flat bread and pita bread.

BREAKFAST CEREALS These include traditional rolled oats, natural muesli and low GI packaged breakfast cereals.

BULGUR WHEAT Use it to make tabbouli, or add to vegetable burgers, stuffings, soups and stews.

CANNED EVAPORATED SKIM MILK This makes an excellent substitution for cream in pasta sauces.

CANNED FISH Keep a good stock of canned tuna packed in spring water, and canned sardines and salmon.

CANNED FRUIT Have a variety of canned fruit on hand, including peaches, pears, apples and nectarines—choose the brands labelled with "no added sugar" fruit juice syrup.

CANNED VEGETABLES* Sweet corn kernels and tomatoes can help to boost the vegetable content of a meal. Tomatoes, in particular, can be used freely because they are rich in antioxidants, as well as having a low GI.

COUSCOUS Ready in minutes, serve with casseroles and braised dishes.

CURRY PASTES A tablespoon or so makes a delicious curry base.

DRIED FRUIT These include apricots, raisins, prunes and apples.

DRIED HERBS Oregano, basil, ground coriander, thyme and rosemary can be useful to have on stand-by in the pantry.

HONEY Those with the lowest GI include the pure floral honeys, not the commercially blended types.

JAM A dollop of good-quality jam (with no added sugar) on toast contains fewer calories than butter or margarine.

LEGUMES Stock a variety of legumes (dried or canned), including lentils, split peas and beans. There are many bean varieties, including cannellini, butter, white, kidney and soy beans.

MUSTARD Seeded or whole grain mustard is useful as a sandwich spread, and in salad dressings and sauces.

*These foods may be high in sodium. Look for reduced-sodium options.

NOODLES Many Asian noodles such as Hokkien, udon and rice vermicelli have low to intermediate GI values because of their dense texture, whether they are made from wheat or rice flour.

NUTS* Try a handful of nuts (about 1 oz or 2 tablespoons) every other day. Try them sprinkled over your breakfast cereal, salad or dessert, and enjoy unsalted nuts as a snack as well.

OILS Try olive oil for general use; some extra-virgin olive oil for salad dressings, marinades and dishes that benefit from its flavor; and sesame oil for Asian-style stir-fries. Canola or olive oil cooking sprays are handy too.

PASTA A great source of carbohydrates and B vitamins. Fresh or dried, the preparation is easy. Simply cook in boiling water until just tender, or al dente, drain and top with your favorite sauce and a sprinkle of Parmesan cheese.

QUINOA This whole grain cooks in about 10–15 minutes and has a slightly chewy texture. It can be used as a substitute for rice, couscous or bulgur wheat. It is very important to rinse the grains thoroughly before cooking.

RICE Basmati, brown, wild or koshihikari varieties have a much lower GI than, for example, jasmine rice.

ROLLED OATS Besides their use in porridge, oats can be added to cakes, muffins, breads and desserts.

SEA SALT Use in moderation.

SPICES Most spices, including ground cumin, turmeric, cinnamon, paprika and nutmeg, should be bought in small quantities because they lose pungency with age and incorrect storage.

STOCK* Make your own stock or buy prepared products, which are available in aseptic containers in the supermarket. To keep the sodium content down with ready-made stocks and bouillon cubes, look out for a low salt option.

TOMATO PASTE Use in soups, sauces and casseroles.

VINEGAR White wine or red wine vinegar and balsamic vinegar are excellent as vinaigrette dressings in salads.

*These foods may be high in sodium. Look for reduced-sodium options.

WHAT TO KEEP IN YOUR REFRIGERATOR

BACON* Bacon is a valuable ingredient in many dishes because of the flavor it offers. You can make a little bacon go a long way by trimming off all fat and chopping it finely. Ham is often a more economical and leaner way to go. In casseroles and soups, a ham or bacon bone imparts a fine flavor, with less fat.

CAPERS, OLIVES AND ANCHOVIES* These can be bought in jars and kept in the refrigerator. They are a tasty addition to pasta dishes, pizzas and salads.

CHEESE* Any reduced fat cheese is great to keep handy in the fridge. A block of Parmesan is indispensable and will keep for up to 1 month. Reduced fat cottage and ricotta cheeses have a short life so are best bought as needed, and they can be a good alternative to butter or margarine in a sandwich.

CONDIMENTS* Keep jars of minced garlic, chile or ginger in the refrigerator to spice up your cooking in an instant.

EGGS To enhance your intake of omega-3 fats, we suggest using omega-3-enriched eggs. Although the yoke is high in cholesterol, the fat in eggs is predominantly monounsaturated, and therefore considered a "good fat."

FISH Try a variety of fresh fish.

FRESH HERBS These are available in most supermarkets and there really is no substitute for the flavor they impart. For variety, try parsley, basil, mint, chives and cilantro.

FRESH FRUIT Almost all fruit make an excellent low GI snack. When in season, try fruit such as apples, oranges, pears, grapes, grapefruit, peaches, apricots, strawberries and mangoes.

JARRED VEGETABLES* Sun-dried tomatoes, olives, roasted eggplant and peppers are handy to keep as flavorsome additions to pastas and sandwiches.

MEAT AND CHICKEN Lean varieties are better—try lean beef, lamb fillets, pork fillets, chicken (breast or drumsticks) and minced beef.

MILK Skim or low-fat milk is best, or try low-fat calcium-enriched soy milk.

VEGETABLES Keep a variety of seasonal vegetables on hand such as spinach, broccoli, cauliflower, Asian greens, asparagus, zucchini and mushrooms. Peppers, scallions and sprouts (mung bean and snowpea sprouts) are great to bulk up a salad. Sweet corn, sweet potato and yam are essential to your low GI food store.

YOGURT Low-fat natural yogurt provides the most calcium for the fewest calories. Have vanilla or fruit versions as a dessert, or use natural yogurt as a condiment in savory dishes. However, if using yogurt in a hot meal, make sure you add it at the last minute, and do not let it boil or it will curdle.

*These foods may be high in sodium. Look for reduced-sodium options.

WHAT TO KEEP IN YOUR FREEZER

FROZEN BERRIES Berries can make any dessert special, and by using frozen ones it means you don't have to wait until berry season in order to indulge. Try berries such as blueberries, raspberries and strawberries.

FROZEN YOGURT This is a fantastic substitute for ice-cream and some products even have a similar creamy texture, but with much less fat.

FROZEN VEGETABLES Keep a packet of peas, beans, corn, spinach or mixed vegetables in the freezer—these are handy to add to a quick meal.

ICE CREAM Reduced or low-fat ice cream is ideal for a quick dessert, served with fresh fruit.

MAKING SENSE OF FOOD LABELING

These days, food labels contain quite a lot of detailed product information, but unfortunately, very few people know how to interpret it correctly. Often the claims on the front of the packet don't mean quite what you think. Here are some prime examples:

CHOLESTEROL FREE Take care, as the food may still be high in fat.

FAT REDUCED Double-check if the product is actually low in fat. Even though the fat may be reduced, it may still be very high.

NO ADDED SUGAR This does not necessarily mean that a product is low in sugar—it could still raise your blood glucose levels.

LITE Check to see exactly what the product is light in. The "lite" could simply mean light in color.

Currently, the United States has no national standard for what constitutes a low GI food. However, you can use the nutrition facts label to help you determine whether a food is a "good-carb" choice. Look for:

• Fiber – Choose foods that provide at least 1–3g of fiber per serving.

• Whole grain – Select foods that list whole grains within the first three ingredients. Whole grains include bulgur (cracked wheat), oats, barley, whole cornmeal, and brown rice.

• Minimal Processing – Limit foods that list milled or processed grains. Milling and grinding remove the fiber-rich outer bran and the vitamin- and mineral-rich inner germ.

Visit www.nutrisystem.com to learn more about the GI and "good-carbs."

ACKNOWLEDGMENTS

A book such as this just doesn't happen. It evolved with the help and inspiration of many individuals. Firstly, we would like to thank the ever cheerful, dedicated and totally tireless production team at Hodder Australia. In particular, our thanks to Fiona Hazard and Anna Waddington for making it all happen; our editor, Kim Rowney, for her commitment and meticulous attention to detail; and Michelle Cutler, for designing a book that is a joy to read. Thanks also to Kathy Hanuschack, RD, LDN, for her work on the North American edition of this book.

We are thrilled with the photography and would like to thank Ian Hofstetter, Stephanie Souvlis and Lee Currie. Thank you also to our lovely models: Anna, Bill, Claudia and Jack, Fiona and Sophie, Joanna and Oliver, Julie, Tania, Tyson and Pia, and Vivien. And for supplying the linen and kitchenware for photography, we would like to thank Cloth, Plenty Homewares, and Wheel and Barrow.

Thank you to Nutrisystem, Inc., for their contributions to this revised edition.

We are deeply indebted to all those who have generously provided delicious recipes for this book. In particular we want to thank:

Johanna Burani, our dedicated US colleague, who has adapted a number of our books for the American market, for Chocolate apple sauce cupcakes, page 116; and Cherry oat crunchies, page 128.

Chris and Carolyn Caldicott (www.worldcafe.com) for Sweet potatoes in ginger, cayenne and peanut sauce, page 102, from *World Food Café*, Bay Books/Soma 1999—a favorite recipe of our North American colleagues, Professor Tom Wolever and his wife, Judy.

Judy Davie (www.thefoodcoach.com.au) for Beefburgers with (tomato and bean) salsa, page 33; and Scottish oatcakes, page 124, from *The Food Coach*, Viking 2004.

Jenny Fanshaw for Soba noodle soup with shrimp and tofu, page 67; and Apple and strawberry crumble, page 127.

Margaret Fulton for Vegetable chili bowl, page 31, from *Margaret Fulton's New Cookbook*, Angus & Robertson 1993.

Liz and Ian Hemphill of Herbies Spices (www.herbies.com.au) for Chachouka, page 28 (with grainy toast), from *Spice Notes*, Macmillan 2000. Tagine spice mix, page 79; Chermoula spice mix, Harissa, and Vindaloo curry powder, page 134, from *Spicery* (with Philippa Sandall), Hardie Grant 2004.

Penny Hunking (www.energise.co.uk), who helped adapt *The Low GI Diet* for the UK, for Barley and vegetable soup, page 55.

Julie Le Clerc (www.julieleclerc.com) for Mustard-roasted fruits, page 16, from *Simple Deli Food*, Penguin Books (NZ) 2002; and Roast pumpkin and chickpea salad, page 52, from *Simple Café Food*, Penguin Books (NZ) 1999.

Dr Nancy Longnecker for Lentil bruschetta, page 27, from *Passion for Pulses*, University of Western Australia Press 2000 (www.uwapress.uwa.edu.au).

Isobel McMillan for Beef stroganoff, page 81; Crunchy-topped lentil loaf, page 103; and Mung bean dhal, page 136.

Jill McMillan for Nasi goreng, page 40; Fragrant bulgur wheat with zest, page 68; and Aduki bean stew, page 83.

Luke Mangan for Chicken, mint and corn soup, page 63; Curried lentil salad, page 64; and Chile corn salsa, page 87.

Lynne Mullins, a regular food writer for the *Sydney Morning Herald's* "Good Living" section for Vietnamese beef soup, page 73; and Chicken and bok choy stir-fry, page 85, from *Noodles to Pasta*, HarperCollins Publishers, 1999.

Emma Pemberton for her refreshing Grapefruit granita, page 130.

Professor Steffan Rössner and his daughter Sofia for their dinner party recipes—Golden carrot soup, page 57; Marinated steaks (ostrich or kangaroo) with Mexican bean salad (served with grilled asparagus and bourbon sauce), page 97; and Italian strawberries, page 112.

Emma Sandall for her delicious Couscous salad, page 62.

Catherine Saxelby (www.foodwatch.com.au), our ever-generous colleague who helped us get started on our publishing program, for Fresh plum and ricotta strudel, page 115; and Apricot oat munchies, page 122, from *Eating for the Healthy Heart*, Hardie Grant Books 2001.

Carol Selva Rajah (www.gourmetasiancuisine.com.au) for her aromatic Pork vindaloo, page 88; Grilled fish tikka, page 91; and Cucumber raita, page 134.

Dr Rosemary Stanton for Toasted muesli, page 13.

Michelle Trute (www.cookingwithconscience.com), passionate GI advocate, for Roasted pumpkin and mushroom lasagne, page 94, from *Cooking with Conscience Book 1*, self published 2002.

Loukie Werle, food writer and food editor for several Australian magazines, for her Smoked salmon and dill with pasta salad, page 58, from *Trattoria Pasta*, Hodder & Stoughton 1993.

INDEX